Science Web Reader

PHYSICS

First published in 2001 by:
Nelson Thornes (Publishers) Ltd
Delta Place
27 Bath Road
CHELTENHAM
GL53 7TH
United Kingdom

05 / 10 9 8 7 6 5 4 3

A catalogue record for this book is available from the British Library

ISBN 0 17 438739 3

Designed and typesetting by Mick Hodson Associates
Photo research by Zooid Pictures Limited

Printed and Bound in Croatia by Zrinski d. d. Cakovec

Author team:

Joan Solomon (Series Editor): Visiting professor at the Open University and King's College London. An experienced author who specialises in history of science and ethics and has written extensively at KS3/KS4.

Jim Henderson: Key Curriculum Leader for Science, Maths and D & T, The Charter School, South London.

Steuart Kellington: Former Principal of Burnley College, Lancashire.

Averil Macdonald: Lecturer in Physics at the University of Reading; Educational Consultant.

Nigel Heslop: Senior Science teacher, Oak Farm School. Consultant and author.

Jonathan Osbourne: Senior Lecturer in Science Education, King's College London.

Mary Ratcliffe: Senior Lecturer in Science Education at the University of Southampton. A-Level Chemistry author and Chair of examiners.

Richard Robinson: Television presenter and writer. Author of a series of books called *Science Magic*.

Every effort has been made to contact copyright holders. The publishers apologise to anyone whose right s have been overlooked and will be happy to rectify any errors or omissions at the earliest opportunity.

Acknowledgements
Corbis UK Ltd. **5t**; Corbis UK Ltd. **5b**; Daily Star/Express Newspapers/*John Frost* **8t**; *Phil Schermeister*/Corbis UK Ltd. **8b**; Bettmann/Corbis UK Ltd. **9**; Bettmann/Corbis UK Ltd. **10t**; Illustrated London News/Hulton Getty Picture Collection Ltd. **10b**; Bettmann/Corbis UK Ltd. **11**; *Jim Sugar*/Corbis UK Ltd. **13t**; *Chinch Gryniewicz*/Ecoscene/Corbis UK Ltd. **13b**; *Dave Bartruff*/Corbis UK Ltd. **14**; Reuters New Media Inc./Corbis UK Ltd. **21l**; Bettmann/Corbis UK Ltd. **21r**; Marks Barfield Architects, Creators of the British Airways London Eye (www.marksbarfield.com). **22t/b**; Reuters New Media Inc./Corbis UK Ltd. **23l**; AFP/Corbis UK Ltd. **23r**; Corel professional photos. **32**; Corbis UK Ltd. **42tl**; Trinity House Lighthouse Service. **43r**; *Bob Rowan*/Progressive Image/Corbis UK Ltd. **44**; *Nik Wheeler*/Corbis UK Ltd. **45t**; *Adam Woolfit*/Corbis UK Ltd. **45c**; *Peter Finger*/Corbis UK Ltd. **45b**; NewScientist (www.newscientist.com). **49l**; AFP/Corbis UK Ltd. **49r**; Bettmann/Corbis UK Ltd. **50c**; Science Photo Library **50b**; Bettmann/Corbis UK ltd. **53tl**; Agfa Belgium **53tr**; *Lester V. Bergman*/Corbis UK Ltd. **53b**; Dept. of Pure Mathematics and Mathematical Statistics/University of Cambridge/British Library **57**; *Paul Almasy*/Corbis UK Ltd. **58l**; *David A. Hardy*/Science Photo Library **58r**; Science Photo Library **59t**; Science Photo Library **59b**; NASA/*Roger Ressmeyer*/Corbis UK Ltd. **60**; Bettmann/Corbis Uk Ltd. **61tl**; NASA/*Roger Ressmeyer*/Corbis UK Ltd. **61bl**; Corbis UK Ltd. **61tr**; NASA/Science Photo Library **61br**; Corbis UK Ltd. **62bl**; Corbis UK Ltd. **62br**; Bettmann/Corbis UK Ltd. **62t**; *Darrell Gulin*/Corbis UK Ltd. **63t**: *Lon E. Lauber*/Oxford Scientific Films **63c**; *David Parker*/Science Photo Library **63b**; Eye of Science/Science Photo Library **64**.

CONTENTS

Foreword

These readers for Science Web are a new departure for science education. They have been written for students of all sorts, for science enthusiasts who want to read more about modern science, for students who are on the humanities side and who like nothing more than curling up with a good story – whether about a scientist or anyone else, and for students who don't usually read much at all but enjoy cartoons and good illustrations. Some of the stories are about exciting new scientific discoveries, some are about scientific explorations in earlier times and a few describe applications of science or technology. They aim to keep school science up to date and interesting.

Teachers will find that the subject matter of each reading passage connects with science in the National Curriculum, even though the stories do not try to teach it in the usual way. Because the stories are related to real people we believe their science content will become more memorable. At the end of each article there is a selection of questions. These might be used by some teachers as part of the homework, or for classwork when students seem to need a quiet spell of self-learning. Other teachers may choose to adapt or even ignore the questions.

We believe that all the articles are suitable for some Key Stage 3 readers. We know that students in these years of schooling have a wide range of reading ages and rather than reduce the language to some lowest common denominator we decided to replicate the natural variety in two ways. Firstly we have provided stories with different styles, some deliberately exciting, some amusing, and some which pursue the search for a solution to some medical or similar problem. Our second way of providing variety is through the illustrations. Our artists have produced exceptionally fine pictures, some of which are quite beautiful. There are also photographs and cartoons.

These readers are designed to spread enthusiasm for science. It is changing so fast that we need to include up-to-the-minute discoveries. The stories from earlier times show that science has always been changing. It is, and was, the product of inventive men and women, so we have included human detail of how different scientists have reacted to challenges. Most importantly, these stories are designed to encourage students to get into the habit of reading about science, and so kindle a lifelong interest in it and in its progress.

Professor Joan Solomon

Series Editor

Science Web Readers

Caroline Herschel

Caroline Herschel was born in Hanover, Germany, in 1750 – a troubled time. When she was only seven years old the French invaded Hanover, her father had died and her older brother William fled to England. Until she was 22 Caroline simply stayed at home and so, when she went to England, she only knew what her mother had taught her.

The Herschels of Windsor!

Meanwhile, William was making his way in England. Now he wanted Caroline to come and keep house for him and to sing in the choir he was running in Bath. Both brother and sister were very musical. Indeed, when Caroline auditioned she was invited to take a part in the Royal Opera in London. But William had become very interested in astronomy and had even discovered a new planet – Uranus. He had been given a medal by the Royal Society, and was made Astronomer to King George III at a salary of £200 per year. This is equivalent to about £50 000 at modern rates! William was delighted and told Caroline that she must come with him to keep house at a place near Windsor where they would build a great new telescope and study the stars. We don't know what Caroline thought about this at first, but she certainly made a great success of astronomy.

Uranus – discovered by William Herschel.

Search for a better telescope

The earliest telescopes that Galileo and others had made had a large convex lens. It had to be large to collect as much of the faint starlight as possible and to focus it on the eyepiece. This magnified the images a bit more and made them brighter. However, as time went by the astronomers found that they had a problem. However careful they were, the big lens seemed to be distorting the image more and more. It was as if the lens was made of jelly and was 'sagging' in the middle! Of course, glass does seem hard, but really it is a cooled-down liquid and, if you only support it round the edge, it does 'sag' a little bit.

William and Caroline wanted to study faint (that is, distant) stars and galaxies. So they needed the images to be as sharp and true as possible. They decided not to use a big glass lens at all, but to grind a huge concave mirror out of metal. William had already experimented with different metals and alloys (mixtures of metals) and had fixed on a combination of copper, tin and antimony in secret proportions. By the time they moved near to Windsor, Caroline and William had a telescope with a perfect shiny metal mirror, ground and polished by Caroline to have an exact point focus. Their largest telescope had a mirror more than one metre wide. The eyepiece lens was also

Caroline Herschel when she was very old.

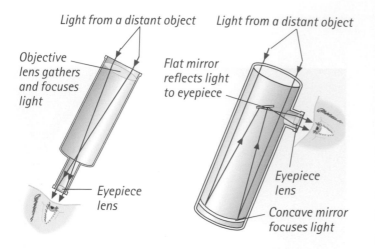

The refracting telescope and the reflecting telescope.

outstanding, having a magnification of up to 5000 times. It was the astronomical wonder of the age!

Joint discoveries

Caroline and William made the first ever discovery of a new planet. At first they did not realise it was a planet, and called it 'Georgium Sidus' in honour of the 'mad' King George III. But then they realised it must be a planet, and called it Uranus, after the father of the Greek god Saturn. All the other planets, from Mercury to Saturn, could be seen with the naked eye and had been found and named by the ancient Indian and Babylonian astronomers. But how do you recognise a planet?

'It should be circling around the Sun.' That seems like an easy answer, but wait a bit. If it is much further out from the Sun than the Earth then it will be travelling slower because the pull of the Sun will be much less. If you are observing it from a comparatively fast moving Earth it might well seem to be moving backwards (see diagram below). But then if we are moving in the opposite direction to that of Uranus, it might seem to be moving faster. (Think of a train passing yours in a station.) Complicated, isn't it? If the astronomer cannot calculate the path of the 'new star' correctly it might seem to be a comet, or a meteor or even a star, instead of a planet being pulled steadily into a roughly circular orbit around the Sun.

The situation called for a really good mathematician. Fortunately, it turned out that Caroline, despite having had almost no schooling, was very clear-headed and better than William at astronomical calculations. He left much of this work to her. Mostly, he did the observations but, when he was away at Court, Caroline got a chance to use the big telescope and she discovered three new nebulae (mainly fuzzy distant galaxies) and eight comets for herself. She had to make her own smaller reflecting telescope for everyday observation.

The universal force

The pull of gravity is more than just the force that keeps

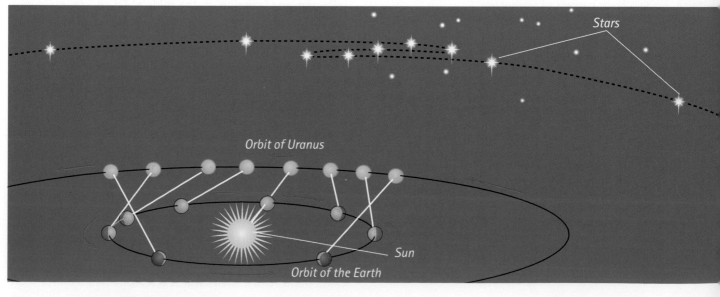

The orbits of Earth and Uranus.

our planets revolving around the Sun. It is a universal force. Each of the planets which have their own moons pull on them with the same kind of force. The Herschels studied the moons of Saturn and other planets, and wrote a book called *The Revolutions of the Planets.* It was important to show that gravity was a universal force. Some while later they had an opportunity to collect more evidence for gravity working on an astronomical scale.

The 'dance' of the stars

William wanted to get a feel for how far away the other stars might be. At the time of Galileo people often complained that if the Earth really did go round the Sun we should be able to tell. Although the Earth might feel stationary all the other stars would seem to move in the opposite direction to us. If you look out of the window of a fast smoothly-driven car, the distant fields near the horizon seem almost stationary, but the fields near you seem to be moving backwards. This effect is called parallax (see diagram below). By the time of the Herschels, no astronomer had yet found any parallax in the stars. Perhaps the stars were all too far away. But the Herschels did find and calculate this strange circular dance in a few close-by stars. It was the ultimate proof that the Earth does go round the Sun, but it was a good century too late for poor old Galileo. He had been tried by a court, and made to state in public that he had been wrong to say that the Earth moved. Caroline and William's work showed that he had NOT been wrong.

When he was observing the stars most closely William found several pairs of stars. We now call them 'double stars', which go round each other. This was another effect of gravity – when each star attracts the other and they go round in a ring.

Caroline went on with the great work of cataloguing all the stars, double stars, planets, and galaxies in the sky. When William died she went home to Hanover but continued with this work, only finishing when she was eighty. She died in 1848, still studying astronomy, at the age of ninety eight!

QUESTIONS

1. Describe some of the effects which are due to:
   a) the gravity of the Sun
   b) the gravity of a planet
   c) the gravity of the Earth
   d) the gravity of a moon.
2. Which part of a telescope is responsible for making the image:
   a) as bright as possible?
   b) as large as possible?
3. Find out about the world's largest optical telescopes, how wide their mirrors are, and where they are built. Why are none of the best optical telescopes found in Britain?

Distant stars.

One nearer star on the tip of the pencil.

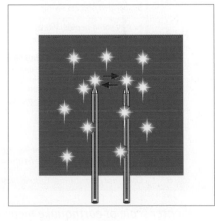

The nearer star seems to move to and fro when you move your head.

Earthquake!

It was a really strange feeling! Suddenly I felt wobbly, the bookshelves in the library seemed to shift slightly and I could hear glass clinking loudly from the science prep room next door. Then, just as suddenly, it stopped.

'What was that all about?' I asked myself. It was 2nd April 1990 and the British Isles had just been hit by an earthquake measuring 5.2 on the Richter Scale.

Luckily there was no damage – except for a broken measuring cylinder. But it made me think. It must be terrifying to be caught in a serious earthquake. First, having no idea what is going on, and then realising there's nothing you can do. Your whole world just comes crashing down.

Clever buildings

Earthquakes are killers. Falling buildings cause most of the deaths. But, interestingly, some buildings will remain standing while those around them come crashing down. Engineers can now design so-called 'clever' buildings, which are much more likely to withstand an earthquake.

Some buildings have 'shock absorbers', like on a car. These are large oil-filled pistons between the floors, which

Britain gets earthquakes too!

squeeze in and out when the building is shaken by an earthquake. This means the building is not thrown about so much (engineers say that its movement is 'damped') so it is less likely to be broken apart and fall down. Other buildings are built on large sliders, so when the foundations are moved by an earthquake, the rest of the building stays still.

Cleverer still is 'active control'. This involves electronic sensors which sense the movement of the ground and a 'feedback' mechanism which steadies the building against the force of the earthquake trying to move it. This is still being tested.

Magnitude (Richter scale)	Effects [§]	Energy (explosive power)	Number of Quakes per Year
0 to 1.9	Recorded by instruments only	Approx. 10.45 kg of TNT	Large number
2 to 2.9	Felt only by the most sensitive. Suspended objects swing	Up to 450 kg TNT	300 000
3 to 3.9	Felt by some people. Vibration like a passing heavy vehicle		49 000
4 to 4.9	Felt by most people. Hanging objects swing. Dishes and windows rattle and may break	Approaching a small atom bomb (20 kilotons)	6 200
5 to 5.9	Felt by all; people frightened. Chimneys topple; furniture moves		800
6 to 6.9	Some panic. Buildings may suffer substantial damage	Minimum of a hydrogen bomb (1 megaton)	120
7 to 7.9	Widespread panic. Few buildings remain standing. Large landslides; fissures in ground	Approx. 100 hydrogen bombs	18
8 to 8.6	Complete devastation. Ground waves	At least 60 000 hydrogen bombs	0.2 (one every few years)

The Richter scale of earthquake measurement. [§]Effects assuming a shallow earthquake in a populated area.

Tall buildings can survive an earthquake.

What's your natural frequency?

Resonance isn't only to do with buildings. Even people's bodies have a natural frequency – they are affected most by vibrations happening at 5 times per second (5 Hertz). This is important for car manufacturers because if a car vibrates at 5 Hertz then the passengers will feel very uncomfortable or even physically sick.

The chance of this happening can be predicted by calculating the Motion Sickness Dose Value. Tests in which volunteers were shaken for up to 6 hours, showed that 70 per cent of people will vomit if shaken between 4-8 times a second.

Vibration-Induced White Finger can also be caused by rapid shaking. This affects people who use machinery which vibrates a lot. The vibrations shake the blood away from the tips of their fingers, which become white and numb. In severe cases, amputation is the only treatment.

The Tacoma Narrows Bridge after shaking in the wind.

Shaken to pieces

How tall a building is makes a difference to whether it falls down in an earthquake. And it's not just the tallest ones which fall! Every building has a 'natural frequency'. This means that it will sway back and forth at a fixed rate. The Empire State Building in New York sways back and forth once every 8 seconds when the wind is in the right direction. If a building is forced to sway at its natural frequency it is like pushing a swing. It just goes further and further and further with each push, until it is moving so much it breaks apart. Scientists call this effect 'resonance'. This happened to a bridge in the USA. The Tacoma Narrows Bridge was famous because it always swayed in the wind, but one day it swung too much, shook itself apart and fell into the river.

If a building is designed so that it won't sway with an earthquake (its natural frequency is different from the rate of ground-shaking caused by an earthquake) then it is less likely to fall down. In Japan they always try to design buildings so that they are the right height and won't sway with an earthquake.

QUESTIONS

1. When scientists design earthquake-proof buildings they sometimes use 'shock absorbers' and 'sliders'. How do these work?
2. One of the latest ideas to help buildings stay up during an earthquake is called 'active control'. How does this work?
3. What is the natural frequency of the Empire State Building?
4. If a building is shaken by the wind or an earthquake at just the right frequency, describe what might happen.
5. What do they do in Japan to make sure their buildings won't fall down in an earthquake?
6. Why is it useful for car manufacturers to know that the natural frequency of the human body is 5 Hertz?
7. What experiment do scientists have to do to find out what causes car passengers to vomit?
8. Why are people who use vibrating machinery in danger of losing one or more fingers?

Inventing electric light

It's easy to think that everybody has electricity and that everyone has electric light. This is not true as only 3 in 10 of the world's population has electricity.

Thomas Edison.

WORLD INEQUALITY

A good way of looking at inequality is to imagine the world as a village of **100** people. There would be:

57 Asians 21 Europeans
14 from the Western Hemisphere
(*North and South America*)
8 Africans

52 would be female 48 would be male
50% of the entire world's wealth would be in the hands of only **6** people and all
6 would be citizens of the United States!

70 would be unable to read
50 would suffer from malnutrition
30 would have electricity
Only **1** would own a computer

From Electric Avenue to Menlo Park

Even those of us who have electric light have had it for less than a 100 years. The first people to have electricity supplied to their homes lived in Brixton in London in a street that is now named 'Electric Avenue'. The popular invention soon spread far and wide. The idea of using electricity to produce light was first developed by Thomas Edison working at Menlo Park near New York. Here is the story of his discovery, told in a book written by his assistant Frances Jehl.

Electric lights illuminating the streets of London.

Chinese and Italian raw silk both boiled out and otherwise treated were amongst the first substances used as filaments in electric lights. The most interesting material of all was the hair of the luxurious beards of some of the men about the laboratory. There was the great 'derby', in which we had a contest between filaments made from the beards of Kruesi and J.U. Mackenzie, to see which would last the longer in a lamp. Bets were placed with much gusto by the supporters of the two men, and many arguments held over the rival merits of their beards.

Kruesi, you know, was a cool mountaineer from Switzerland possessed of a bushy, black beard. Mackenzie was the station master at Mt. Clements, Michigan, who had taught telegraphy to the chief in the early days after the young Edison had saved the life of Mackenzie's small son Jimmy. His beard, or rather, his sideburns, were stiff and bristling.

As I now recall, he won the contest, though some claimed that he had an unfair advantage; that less current was used on the filament made from his hair than on that from Kruesi's. Be that as it may, both burned out with considerable rapidity.

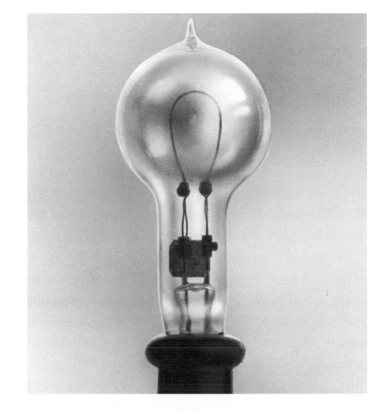

Edison's light bulb.

At last, on 21 October, 1879, Edison made a bulb that did not burn out. Its filament was of carbonised cotton sewing thread, and Edison and Jehl sat up all night watching it shine. The first commercial bulb, which followed swiftly, had a horseshoe filament of carbonised paper. *The New York Herald* reporter, Marshall Fox, visited the laboratory and explained how the filament was prepared.

Edison's electric light, incredible as it may appear, is produced from a little piece of paper – a tiny strip of paper that a breath would blow away. Through this little strip is passed an electric current, and the result is a bright, beautiful light, like the mellow sunset of an Italian autumn.

'But paper instantly burns, even under the trifling heat of a tallow candle!' exclaims the sceptic, 'and how, then, can it withstand the fierce heat of an electric current?' Adapted from *Inventing Electric Light* in the *Faber Book of Science* and drawn from *Menlo Park Reminiscences*, by Francis Jehl. Edison Institute, Dearborn, Michigan.

QUESTIONS

1. Things that get hot normally burn. Why does the filament of the electric light bulb not burn up?
2. The light from a bulb is normally yellow. That from the Sun is much whiter. Why is this?
3. In those days, Edison couldn't use the easily available metals for his filament, like iron or copper? Why not? What do you think would have happened if he had used them?
4. What would be the likely effect on the brightness of the bulb of making the filament thicker?
5. Fluorescent strip lights do not have a thin wire in them and they produce a very different kind of light. What advantages do they have over normal light bulbs? Find out how they work.
6. The paper had been 'carbonised' – that is baked in an oven first so that only the carbon in the paper is left. What are the two common forms of carbon found in nature?

Energy – an eternal delight?

Jenny was looking at a strange exhibit in a remote corner of the Electricity Gallery. She called her mother over to the display hologram and pointed at what looked like a rough black lump of flaky rock. 'What's that, mum?' she asked, putting on a sensor glove to explore the powdery surface of the virtual exhibit. Annoyingly, her mother, Ms Franklin, was one of those parents who never gives a straight answer to anything. 'Try putting it into the virtual laboratory tester, Jenny, and see what it does.' So Jenny manipulated the virtual black lump into a dish. She saw it burst into flames and, as she moved the sensor glove above it, she felt a sharp painful burning sensation and withdrew her hand quickly. As she watched, she saw a tank of water appear above the flames. The water started to bubble and boil and the steam went rushing through a pipe towards what looked like a big propeller. This began to spin and turn another device to which it was connected by a metal rod. Jenny's mother decided to give Jenny a bit of help at

Jenny examines the exibit in a virtual tester.

this point and swiped her parent card to instruct the display to explain what was happening. A sign gradually came into focus:

'The steam spins the turbine. The turbine drives the generator which turns the movement energy into electrical energy.'

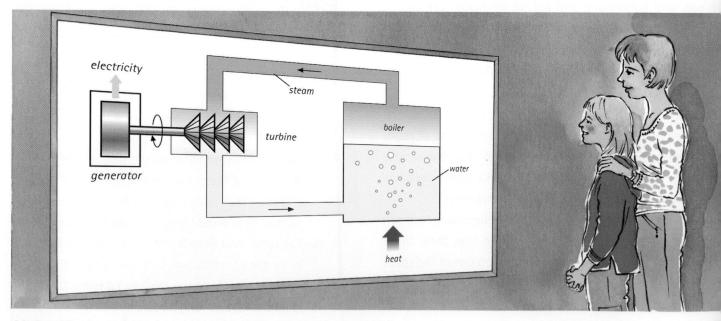

12   *Ms Franklin shows Jenny how a steam turbine generates electricity.*

Energy from the Sun

Jenny's dad had even taken her up onto their roof to remove one of the solar tiles. Jenny was always amazed that their next-door neighbours, the Joneses, didn't have them. The tiles on the two houses looked an almost identical dark grey colour but the ones on the Franklin roof were made from sheets of silicon and stainless steel. Jenny's dad explained how each roof tile acted as a photovoltaic cell, just like the ones that powered Jenny's calculator, turning sunlight energy into an electric current to supply the house.

Jenny was in the same class as Peter Jones from next door and thought it was very funny when they were both asked to bring in an electricity bill from home. During the previous three months the Joneses had paid £350 for their electricity while the Franklins had actually generated more electricity than they needed and had sold the extra to the electricity company – their bill had arrived with a cheque for £130! Jenny regretted telling her dad this because now, every time her dad saw Mr Jones, he would shout out loud, 'Do you want to buy any electricity, George? We couldn't touch another drop.'

Tidal power station on the River Rance.

Electricity from the tides

Jenny was very confused. She had learnt about electricity at school when her class had done projects on how electricity can be produced. Jenny's group had visited the web-site of TidePower. They are the company that built the dam across the estuary of the River Avon near Bristol. They generate electricity by using the potential energy of the water from the Atlantic as it rises and falls with the tide. Jenny had used the special viewing goggles to go up to the 3-D image of the dam wall and watch the water in the river being held back as the Atlantic tide fell. She was even given the option to decide the best time to open the dam gates and let the water pour through the pipes leading from the river back into the ocean. The roar of the water was deafening, but she could see the massive turbines being spun round energetically by the power of the rushing water. The display told her that she had successfully converted 13 per cent of the water's potential energy into electrical energy. She had thought this a bit disappointing until she was told that the maximum efficiency that could be achieved using computer-control of the water flow was only 17 per cent. This sounded rather low but TidePower's virtual guide had pointed out that it was essentially free energy and the engineers were looking at ways of improving the efficiency further.

Solar cells on a roof.

Wind power

During the class presentations Jenny had also learnt about electricity produced from the wind by massive great windmills. There was a whole village in Norfolk that had all of its electricity supplied by one big wind turbine towering above the supermarket at the edge of the village. She knew that some places like Iceland could use the energy from hot rocks under the ground to produce steam for their turbines. And in countries like Scotland the water in high mountain lakes was sent pouring down pipes to drive turbines in a similar way to her tidal power experience.

A problem with waste

Her teacher had even taught them about nuclear power stations. The last of these in Britain had been shut down ten years ago. With so many clean ways of producing electricity the potential health risks from these nuclear power stations was just not worth taking. Some other countries in the world, especially those with access to the uranium that was needed, still produced a lot of their energy that way. However, the Worldwide Environmen Council was trying to stop this. They imposed a Globa Pollution Tax on these countries to pay for the cost o shutting down the power stations and dealing with the radioactive waste materials. They even used some of the money raised to help these countries build clean renewable systems for their energy needs.

But for the life of her, Jenny could not understand wha this display in the Electricity Gallery was about. She explained her puzzlement about the black lump to her mum. Her mum gave the sort of sigh that Jenny knew meant 'Don't they teach you anything at school these days?

Wind turbines capture the wind's energy.

QUESTIONS

1. What is the black flaky rock on display?
2. Name the two other main fossil fuels that we use to produce electricity.
3. What do we mean when we talk about renewable energy?
4. Draw a block diagram to show the main steps in turning a fossil fuel into electricity.
5. This story is set in the future. How many years into the future do you think it is? Explain the reasons for your answer.
6. The passage talks about different forms of energy. For example, the water at high tide has more potential energy. List as many examples of different forms of energy as you can.
7. Try to find out more about geothermal energy and hydroelectric energy.
8. What do you think might be some of the problems about relying on solar power in Britain?
9. Ms Franklin is talking about the virtual museum display to Jenny. Write a script for their conversation which describes what happened to the fossil fuels and the advantages of using the new types of energy technology.

Energy for living in the Alps

John and Chris were walking to Nice through the French Alps, in July. They had left Auron a few days before. They had walked to the high plateau (or plain) of Longon. Look at the map and find Nice, Auron and the Plateau de Longon. The Plateau de Longon is at 1883 metres above sea level. This is almost twice as high as the highest mountains in England and Wales. Snow covers the plateau from October to May.

John and Chris reached the mountain hostel called 'Le Refuge de Longon'. In English this means 'The Refuge at Longon'. Look at the photographs of the refuge. Walkers can stay for the night and buy meals. It's like a simple Youth Hostel. But this refuge also has a herd of dairy cows!

André is the warden of the Refuge and he is helped by his wife Jeanne. They have a baby called Marc. They live at the Refuge from May to September. It is closed for the other months. The refuge is four miles from the nearest village and there is no road. There are no electricity cables and no telephone links. So how can André and Jeanne look after walkers and cows in such a remote place? Let us

John and Chris's route to Nice.

think about their energy needs and how they can be met.

In summer there is plenty of sunshine in the Alps. There is also a stream flowing by the Refuge. A spring nearby provides plenty of good drinking water. Sunshine and water encourage lots of grass to grow. There are also trees near the Refuge. But little else is there to provide energy for living.

Le Refuge de Longon.

Solar panels on the roof of the Refuge.

	ENERGY NEEDS AT THE REFUGE
Energy for lighting	Electrical energy is good for lighting. At home we have lamps which use electricity at 240 V (V is short for volts). Radios, TVs and washing machines also use electricity. André and Jeanne have a radio, but neither a TV nor washing machine.
Energy for cooking	At home you may use electricity or gas for cooking. Some homes have a stove for cooking, which burns wood or coal.
Energy for refrigeration	André needs a big fridge to store food. He cannot run down to the supermarket! Fridges use either electricity or gas.
Energy for heating	It is cool in the Refuge in May, June and September. Electricity, gas, coal and wood are all used for heating.
Energy for communication	André needs to talk to people who want to stay in the Refuge. He needs a telephone. But there are no telephone lines and mobile phones do not work on the plateau.
Energy for milking	André has to milk 30 dairy cows twice every day. Milking by hand would take far too long. He often has to milk the cows away from the Refuge. He needs an electricity generator which he can easily move around.

Milking the cows.

Bottle of propane gas.

Electricity generator.

Storage cells for electrical energy.

	ENERGY SOURCES AT THE REFUGE
Propane gas	Look at the photograph of the big bottle of propane gas. Can you see the metal frame holding the bottle? A helicopter brings in a full bottle of propane gas each month. Gas is used for cooking, for the fridges, for sterilising milk, and making cheese.
Petrol	Look at the photograph of the electricity generator. It is used to generate electricity from petrol for milking the cows. The generator can easily be moved round with the cows.
Wood	Wood is collected from around the Refuge to burn for heating rooms and heating water. Only fallen branches and trees are collected.
Food	A helicopter drops food supplies each month. Food which cannot be stored for a month has to be fetched from the village 7 kilometres (4 miles) away. A donkey is used to carry food, or someone carries it using a big rucksack. The cows give milk and cream and cheese is made from the cream.
Energy from the Sun	Solar power is used to produce electricity for lighting, the radio and the radio-telephone. Look at the photograph of the large solar panels on the roof of the Refuge. Electricity from the solar panels is used by the radio-telephone. The panels give electricity at 24 V directly from the Sun's light energy. But the panels only work during day time, of course. You can see the big storage cells in the plastic bin. Electricity from the solar panels is stored in these cells and electrical energy can then be taken from the cells during the night. A special electronic box near the cells changes the voltage of the electricity from 24 V to 220 V so that it can be used for the lamps and the radio.

Activity	Kind of energy needed	Energy source	Reason for choice of energy source
milking	electricity	petrol	petrol needed to fuel electricity generator to operate pump for milking cows

QUESTIONS

1. Make a list of the energy sources already on the Plateau de Longon.
2. List energy sources brought to the Refuge.
3. Draw a table like the one above and complete it for these activities:
   keeping food in a fridge, sterilising milk, cooking food, heating water, making radio-telephone calls, making cheese, lighting lamps.
4. If the solar panels stopped working, how could the Refuge make light?
5. Why do each of the light switches have a timer which switches off the light after two minutes?
6. Why are the solar panels not used for heating water? (You may need to read the article 'Solar panels around the world', (page 41), to answer this question).
7. Why do the solar panels need a 'special electronic box' so that electric lamps will work?
8. Write a story about a day in the life of Jeanne, the warden's wife. Remember about baby Marc, washing clothes, and fetching food.

I want an anti-gravity mat for Christmas

I am a gravity freak. I admit it. My older brother, Tony, thinks I've totally lost it, and my younger sister, Susan, doesn't really understand. I first got this idea about a year ago. I thought 'Well there are anti-static mats, why not anti-gravity mats as well?' This is what I have in mind. The mat might be about 2 m long and 1 m wide. I'd just put it down on the floor and then, above it, everything would be weightless. GREAT! (I'm not sure if I can just unroll it on the floor, or whether I would have to tack it down to make sure it stays put. I'm still working on that one!)

Which way is 'up'?

Mostly, when I am lying in bed, I think about being weightless above my mat. I could sleep at any angle – vertically, diagonally, or even upside down. Having my hea[d] downwards (or being 'out of my head' as Tony frequentl[y] says) would be much better than doing handstands in th[e] gym. The blood wouldn't rush to your head and make you[r] ears ring. No gravity, so no blood rushing to the head.

Well, I do know that creates a problem. Would I kno[w] which way was up and which was down? I would recognis[e] the ceiling from the floor because of gravity. I would look 'up[' to the ceiling. But no gravity, no 'up'. I think about this a lo[t] when I'm in bed, and now I guess that my room might seem t[o] flip from up to down and back again. It might be like th[e] illusion of the staircase. Do you know that one? First it looks a[s] though you are above it, then it looks like you are underneath[. Try it out.

Sausage in space?

The next problem is how to sleep, and how to move about[. Did you know that when astronauts sleep in space thei[r] arms move up? That's weird! Apparently it is normal Eart[h] gravity which keeps our arms down; without it they woul[d] go up and wave about! So I would have to strap my arm[s]

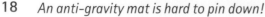

18   *An anti-gravity mat is hard to pin down!*

Reversing staircase illusion.

o my waist. No great problem there. But would I be able to roll over or move about when suspended like a sausage in space? I might not be able to touch the walls and get a good push-off. I worry about this.

Susan, who is really into ballet, suggests that I pull in my arms and legs which, she says, makes you spin round. It sounds stupid, I know, but it is always a mistake to believe that Susan is as silly as she sounds. We tried it out on our neighbour's revolving chair and it worked. If you go round slowly and then 'pull in', you do go round faster!

The gravity-free rope trick

I still worry about moving about in zero gravity. About a month ago, I had this brilliant idea. The astronauts have ropes for pulling on, so I thought I would have a rope hanging down from the ceiling above my anti-gravity mat. Then I could pull myself up to the ceiling. Well, it would hardly be 'pulling'. With no gravity, all I would need is to pull very gently, otherwise I might crash into the ceiling and knock myself out! There are two minor problems here. One is, the rope would not hang 'down'. I would have to be careful what position it was in when I unrolled my mat. The second problem has only just occurred to me. Because

Pull your arms in to spin faster.

a rope is made by twisting fibres together, would it untwist if there was no gravity to hold it down? That is rather like the problem with my arms. Maybe the solution is not to use a rope. I'll have to think about this.

Walking on the Moon

Last summer we had a holiday by the sea. There were huge sand dunes there and jumping down them was great fun. Even the usually superior Tony joined in for a bit! I discovered that if the sand dune was high and the sand was loose, you could leap down in great, long steps and it felt just like zero gravity! Actually, it felt more like the Moon's gravity, which I can tell you is one sixth of Earth's gravity. As you fell the sand fell with you, and your foot touched down on moving sand so that it was always a long slow landing. It felt like being an astronaut – Neil Armstrong or Buzz Aldrin. I tried to tell Tony and Susan about it, but Tony refused to listen and Susan didn't understand. Families are so awful sometimes!

Can you pull yourself 'up' a rope above an anti-gravity mat.

Buzz Aldrin repeated Galileo's experiment on the Moon – dropping a hammer and a feather at the same time.

I've seen videos of the astronauts on the Moon. You know how slowly they dance about? That is because there is so little gravity. The odd thing was that when Buzz Aldrin dropped a feather and a hammer side by side, both reached the Moon's surface (slowly of course) at exactly the same time! It was a surprise to me until I saw two guys diving off the top board together and reaching the water together in the local swimming pool. So it happens with Earth gravity as well. We tried it out by Susan dropping a biro and I a plastic bag of water out of our top-floor window at the same time, into the garden. Both landed exactly together

and the bag of water exploded. It narrowly missed m[y] mother who looked up, but I managed to pull Susan dow[n] behind me. There was trouble!

Moon jumping

Last night I stayed awake for ages thinking about falling and the Moon. I wondered what would happen if Susa[n] and I jumped at the same time. I think we would stay sid[e] by side, wouldn't we? And if I was carrying my school ba[g] and let go of it when I jumped, it would also fall side b[y] side with us – right? So, I think, for me and Susan it woul[d] be like having no gravity at all. What do you think?

Then, later, I had another thought. You know thos[e] astronauts have to wear helmets and oxygen cylinder[s] because there is no air on the Moon? Well I have [to] worry that this may be because the force of gravit[y] there is so small. I even asked our science teacher, wh[o] answered without making the usual unfunny jokes, an[d] said 'Yes'. Now I have another problem. Would all the ai[r] in my bedroom disappear? Would it go out of m[y] bedroom window? I might suffocate! Help!

QUESTIONS

1. Explain how Australians can walk 'upside down?' in their country.
2. Give your opinion on the questions asked in the last two paragraphs.
3. A feather and a hammer do not drop at the same rate on the Earth. Try it out (keeping your feet out of the way of the falling hammer!). Why is this?

The big wheel keeps on turning

Next time you are riding your bike, look carefully at a wheel. Its design is very clever. All those spokes have to support the weight of you and the bike frame while remaining as thin as possible themselves. Now imagine scaling up that wheel more than 200 times so that it stands over twice as high as the Big Ben clocktower in London! You start to have an idea of the daring behind the design and engineering of the Millennium Wheel or London Eye on the south bank of the River Thames.

The wheel, which stands a massive 135 metres high above the river, started turning at the push of a button by Tony Blair on New Year's Eve, 1999. But the idea for it began as a scrappy drawing some five years earlier when London architects Julia Barfield and David Marks first started to imagine what landmark could be built in London to celebrate the start of the new millennium.

The Millennium Wheel stands a massive 135 metres high, on the south bank of the River Thames.

Ferris and his wheel

The wheel is often called a Ferris Wheel but this is not the correct name to use. A man called George Washington Ferris designed and built the world's first Ferris Wheel for

George Washington Ferris's first wheel, built in Chicago in 1893.

the World's Columbian Exposition in Chicago in 1893. This wheel had the typical hanging baskets that you are probably familiar with from fairground rides.

Unique design

But the design of the Millennium Wheel is unique and different in two ways. Unlike Ferris's wheel it is only supported on one side. The architects designed it this way so that riders would feel they were floating over the river.

21

And the 32 capsules, as the glass pods which carry the riders are called, do not hang down but are supported so that they are always on the outside of the wheel. This guarantees that riders get an unobstructed view all the way round. The more correct term for it is therefore an 'observation wheel'.

These unique features give the ride its particular thrilling sensation, but caused headaches for the engineers for two reasons.

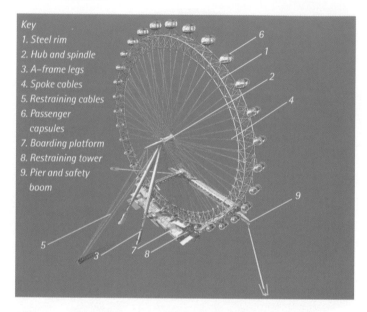

Key
1. Steel rim
2. Hub and spindle
3. A–frame legs
4. Spoke cables
5. Restraining cables
6. Passenger capsules
7. Boarding platform
8. Restraining tower
9. Pier and safety boom

Labelled diagram of the Millennium Wheel (with key).

22 *Rough sketch of the Millennium Wheel, 1993.*

Single-sided support

First, the mass of the whole wheel is 1600 tonnes (1 tonne = 1000 kg). Since 1 kg on Earth has a weight, or force of gravity, of roughly 10 newtons acting on it you might be able to calculate that the weight of the wheel is 16 million newtons. This means that if the wheel is supported on both sides then each support has to cope with a force on it of 8 million newtons. With the support on one side only it means that this one support has to take the whole weight. But, even more awkwardly, it means that the weight of the wheel will try to create a turning effect on the whole structure as it pivots at the point where the support legs go into the ground. This turning effect or moment of the wheel creates the risk that the whole structure might tip into the Thames. To counter this the engineers did two things. They buried the support legs with foundations 40 m deep to oppose the moment of the wheel and they rested the base of the wheel on rollers to cradle it underneath.

External capsules

Second, if you think for a moment, you will realise the challenge facing the other engineers. If the capsules are all fixed in place then, as the wheel turns, so will the capsule and all the passengers will be tipped upsidedown. To prevent this, the engineers had to design a very complicated system of gears to force each capsule to rotate in its enclosure as it goes round the wheel so that it stays upright. On the launch date of 31st December 1999 one of the capsules was sticking and sadly, on safety grounds, no one was allowed on it that night.

The Millennium Wheel is an incredible achievement in terms of design, engineering and organisation. Its 32 capsules can carry a maximum total of 800 people, thus adding another half-million newtons of weight to the structure. The wheel turns continuously at a speed of 0.26 metres per second, which is about a fifth of normal walking speed. So the riders just walk into and out of the capsules as they pass the bottom. The total ride time is 30 minutes for one revolution and the view from the top on a clear day can be as much as 40 km.

Very precise skills were needed to manufacture curved glass that did not distort the view.

The wheel was assembled horizontally, before being winched into place.

An international project

But perhaps the most spectacular triumph of the whole project is the international co-operation it demanded. The architects searched throughout Europe for the best companies to do each part of the job. The main wheel structure was made in three sections in Holland. The enormous hub and spindle around which the wheel rotates was cast at the Skoda factory in the Czech Republic. The bearings came from Germany and the cables from Italy. The capsules were made by a French company called Poma, who normally make cable cars. Perhaps you can see the resemblance. As it was so critical that the beautifully curved glass panels of the capsules did not distort the view, Poma in turn went to a specialist glass company in Venice, Italy, who could supply glass that could be moulded into shape while staying undistorted and strong.

Construction nightmare

All these parts and sections were made in these different places and then finally in the autumn of 1999 they were floated down the Thames on barges to huge platforms in the river where the rim sections and cables were put together. A huge crane was then used to raise the wheel into position. Finally, the capsules were brought up-river and attached one by one. If any of the companies had built any part the wrong size by just a few centimetres the pieces would not have

joined together. But the care taken in producing the design drawings and the expertise of the many engineers made sure that it all slotted together perfectly.

And there it stands now on the bank of the Thames; a moving symbol of what can be achieved by people working in many different countries, using expertise in a great range of science and engineering specialisms. And for Julia Barfield and David Marks, looking at a design that 5 years earlier was just a scribbled sketch on a piece of paper, the thrill and pride of seeing their wheel turning must be amazing.

QUESTIONS

1. Draw a very rough sketch for a Ferris wheel. Think about some of the problems you might have if you actually wanted to build it. What parts would you need for it? Who would make them? How would you get them to the building site? How would you build the wheel?
2. Look at the early sketch by the architects of the Millennium Wheel and compare it to the computer drawing of the final wheel. What differences can you see?. Do you have any theories about why the changes might have been made?
3. Draw a series of simple diagrams to help explain the problem of supporting the wheel and how it was solved.

Mountains of the Moon

No one is quite sure when glass lenses were first invented. There have always been some people who needed spectacles. In early times they must have had to go through life seeing things blurred all the time.

In the Middle Ages, not many people, apart from monks, could read. At that time there were no printing presses and every book had to be copied by hand! This was done by the monks, who often decorated the pages with highly detailed drawings – a great strain for someone with bad eyesight.

The earliest picture of a person wearing glasses is of a monk, in 1352 AD.

About the year 1600, several Dutch inventors hit on the same idea at about the same time. They found that if you put two lenses at the right distance apart, you could make far away things look closer to you. They called this invention the telescope. 'Telescope' means distant seeing.

The first telescopes were not very good and only had a magnifying power of three – this means that things looked three times the size they would have done without the telescope. They were hardly better than toys, but they became a great success. Within six months they were on sale in Paris.

*W*hen an Italian professor of mathematics, called Galileo, heard about telescopes he tried to make his own. Galileo was not only brilliant at mathematics, he was also very good at making things. This was important because in those days you could not go out and buy lenses. You had to make your own. That meant grinding glass until exactly the right shape was formed.

*I*f a lens is not perfectly curved what you see through it is either blurred or twisted. Galileo knew this. With great enthusiasm he set about making the best lenses that he could. By the year 1609 he had made a telescope with a magnifying power of 10.

*G*alileo offered his new telescope to the ruler of Venice and his advisers. He told them how useful it would be for watching out for the approach of enemy ships. They were delighted. He wrote later that even the older senators kept taking it up to the top of the cathedral to look at distant ships.

*G*alileo was given a rise in pay. Galileo went on improving his telescope until it had a magnifying power of 20 times.

One November night, Galileo pointed his latest telescope at the sky. What he saw was amazing! Not only were there far more stars than anyone had ever seen before, but the Moon looked surprisingly different. Each night he observed it very carefully and made diagrams.

*T*he Moon was covered with mountains and valleys. 'It looks rather like the Earth', he wrote to a friend. It also had a lot of round craters as if there had been enormous volcanoes on the Moon.

*G*alileo looked very carefully at the line between the lit-up surface of the Moon and the dark part. This is where it would be late evening on the Moon, with shadows at their longest. Sure enough, along this region between light and dark, Galileo could see shadows.

*O*n the Moon the 'day' is two weeks long and the 'night' is the same. So evening may last for several days. Galileo watched the shadows night after night. He could see that they were growing longer inside the deep craters, and beyond the rocky mountains, as the Sun was slowly setting.

*G*alileo took measurements of the lengths of the shadows and worked out that some of the mountains must be about 4 kilometres (2.5 miles) high! Our Mount Everest is only about 5 kilometres (3 miles) high, even though the Earth is so much bigger. He realised that the Moon had a very rocky and jagged landscape for its size. He could also tell that the shadows always pointed away from the Sun, as though it was sunlight which was making them.

*W*hat struck Galileo most was that the Moon was not perfect and smooth. Poets had written about the Moon being peaceful and shining with its own light, but Galileo did not think this was the case. He thought it was another world lit up by the Sun.

*M*any religious people thought that the Moon was in God's heavens so it had to be smooth, bright and perfect. Galileo had to be careful not to upset their feelings.

He wrote a book called The Starry Messenger about all he had seen through his telescope, and included his own drawings of the Moon. Galileo enjoyed drawing. He said that if he had not been a mathematician and a scientist he would have liked to have been an artist!

Galileo gave names to these dark 'seas'. Even though we now know today that they are not seas we still use the names he gave them. The dry, dark plain where the American astronauts landed in 1969 is still called 'The Sea of Tranquility', as Galileo named it 360 years before.

'The lunar surface is decorated with spots like the dark blue eyes in the tail of a peacock. The larger spots are not filled with mountains and craters but seem to be smoother. So you could call the bright parts "land" and the darker parts "seas".'

QUESTIONS

1. What happens to the length of a shadow as the Sun begins to set on the Moon?
2. Why is it harder to see the shadows of the Moon's craters at a full moon rather than a half moon?
3. What kind of telescope did Galileo make?
4. How would Galileo have worked out the height of the mountains from the length of their shadows?
5. Draw a diagram from the photograph of the Moon and put in the main craters and mountain ranges that you can see.

Mad inventors

Mad inventors appear mad for a very good reason – they're paranoid! They're scared to death that someone is going to steal their invention and take all the credit (and all the profits, too, if it's a money-spinner!) So when you talk with them they might tell you about this or that brilliant idea that's going to revolutionise our lives, but they won't show you it, oh no! Once an idea is out, anyone can hear about it and steal it.

How do you stop someone stealing your idea? Get a patent! Modern Patent Law dates from 1624. It was set up to protect the rights of inventors. If you write to the Patent Office with your idea and a small fee they'll check that it is completely new, and not just like someone else's invention, then announce it publicly, so everyone knows you thought of it first. That way, nobody else can steal it.

Mad inventor.

Pop-up cracker

Patents are granted for new ideas at a rate of dozens a week. Here are a few recent ones. Do you think they'l make their inventors a fortune?

The pop-up cracker.

Ivan Taylor thought of the Christmas card-cracker – a cracker which folds flat like a Christmas card, then springs into shape when removed from the envelope. You can pull it just like an ordinary cracker. He filed it a patent no. GB2 325 866, so now he is free to make as much money from it as he likes. Do you think it's a 'cracker' of an idea?

Jolly lolly

Elliot Rudell has invented the musical lollipop. A tin

The musical lollipop.

speaker and lamp are embedded in the ice, with a wire going down the handle. When a child licks the lolly, he or she completes the electric circuit, and the lolly lights up and plays music. What a simple idea! But don't try to do it yourself; Elliot has patented it (WO 98/45747). The question is, will Elliot make a lot of lolly?

Pen pal

Anyone who has discovered that a ballpoint pen will only work while pointing downwards will queue up to buy a new invention which allows pens to be used upside-down without drying out. Normally the ink is gravity-fed to the tip of the pen. Of course if the pen is tilted upwards gravity can't do its job. The clever inventor has created a separate housing for the ink tube. When you hold the pen sideways the ink tube springs upwards to keep the tip fed with ink.

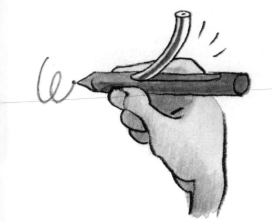

The upside-down pen.

Micro-toothbrush

Toothbrush manufacturers are constantly looking for new gimmicks in their rather dull product. They'll no doubt be rushing to see a new invention by Paul Welfle – a tongue-operated toothbrush. The tiny rotating brush and its motor are mounted on a concave cup, which sits on the end of the tongue. Suction keeps the brush on the tongue, allowing it to get to the parts of the mouth regular brushing cannot reach. So now you

A toothbrush on the top of your toungue.

can spend all day cleaning your teeth without anybody knowing.

Secret snooper

Spying equipment gets smaller and smaller as the technology becomes more refined. The latest bugging device does away with the microphone altogether. The trick lies in realising that when you talk the whole room vibrates, and in particular, the window. When sound waves crash into any surface they make it throb. The effect is easy to spot if you hold a piece of paper against your mouth as you speak – the paper vibrates and tickles your mouth. The

Laser listener.

A skier's breathing tube.

same is true when the sound hits the window. Of course the amount of vibration is tiny, but the latest snooping device uses a laser beam reflecting off the window to detect it and convert it back to speech.

Take a breather

Thomas Crowley was puzzling one night over a problem faced by skiers buried by avalanches in the Alps – they often die of suffocation before rescuers can dig them out, even though the snow around them is full of air. The problem is that the nose and mouth can only take air from the area immediately around them, and warm breath melts the snow, which refreezes into an icy mask over the victim's face. Crowley's idea was simple, but brilliant. A wide sack is attached to the front of the ski jacket, with a tube to the mouth. Now air can be extracted from a wide front. Then another tube takes the exhaled air away to behind the skier's back. In experiments, it has been shown to keep victims well supplied with air for an hour, generally long enough for rescue teams to find them.

Can you think of an invention yourself? Everyone is supposed to have at least one brilliant idea inside them, waiting to get out!

QUESTIONS

1. There are millions of car tyres sitting in dumps all over the world. Can you think of something to do with them?
2. What can you do with all the spare plastic credit cards on the planet?
3. Film canisters look useful, so why do we always throw them away? Think of an invention that uses them.

Taking a barometer up the mountain

The first person to make a barometer was Torricelli, an Italian mathematician. As a young man he read Galileo's books and became so excited by them that he travelled all the way to Florence to meet him. By now Galileo was an old man, totally blind, forbidden to write any more books or to drink red wine. But it was hard to stop Galileo doing anything he wanted to! He was keen on science and he loved wine. He still had new ideas and wanted to write, so Torricelli offered to write to his dictation. For the last three months of Galileo's life that was just what he did, and that was when many of the arguments about barometers took place.

Riddle of the tubes

Galileo knew that if you filled a long tube about 10 metres long with water and then turned it upside down in a jar of water, most of the water stayed in. He had a tube like this fixed to the side of a high tower. But at the top of the tube there was always a space. Galileo talked to Torricelli about

Air pressure can support a 10 metre column of water.

using other liquids instead of water. He thought that the height of liquid had something to do with how heavy it was. So, the height of liquid in the tube might be less with a 'heavy' liquid like mercury, but more with the wine, and still more with light olive oil. The old man was slowly dying, but he went on talking about science and how everyone is free to think about scientific problems and to take measurements for themselves. And then he died.

Soon Torricelli was made mathematician to the Grand Duke of Florence, and Professor of Mathematics at the academy, just as Galileo had been. He decided to carry on with his master's work on barometers, but to use mercury in a much shorter tube, as Galileo had suggested. Once he got a strong enough glass tube the experiment worked wonderfully well. The silver liquid stood about 76cm high, with an empty space above it. But was it really an empty space? Some philosophers thought that it would be quite impossible to have a vacuum. What was happening?

What's in the space?

Galileo had warned Torricelli that recognising a vacuum, which is bound to look just as invisible as air, would be the real problem. But he need not have worried. Torricelli had an idea of his own which was as brilliant and original as any of Galileo's. He was not looking so much inside the tube, as to the pressure of air on the outside. In the clear air of Florence in the evening, just after the Sun set, he could see the atmosphere lit up to a height of at least 50 miles. You try the same, looking west in the evening. How high is the reddish colour? This is what he wrote:

'We live at the bottom of a great ocean of air. We know that air has weight and Galileo measured it at ground level. Higher up it probably weighs less still. But there is so much of it that it will support quite a weight of liquid.'

31

How high does the air extend upwards?

What is the pressure of the air?

Torricelli predicted that it would not matter how long the tube was, the pressure of the great ocean of air, pushing down on the surface of the mercury, would always support the same amount of this heavy liquid – usually 76 cm. He proved this too.

Torricelli was a bit disappointed. He had a hunch that the height of the barometer would change with the weather, it might be higher in fine weather, and lower when it was damp because moist air has less density. But he could never quite prove this with his barometer. Torricelli died when he was only 39, with the problem still unsolved.

Pascal's challenge

The next mathematician to take up the puzzle was a French professor called Blaise Pascal. The first thing he did was to set up some barometers, filled with wine, water, oil and mercury, in front of a lot of educated people. Just as Torricelli had predicted there was more of the lighter liquids like wine and oil supported in the tubes, but less water, and much less mercury. Every barometer tube also had a vacuum at the top – if that's what it was.

Still people were not convinced. (What a waste of a

Perrier setting off up the mountain with five important people.

Perrier setting up a second barometer at the top of the mountain.

that good wine – as Galileo might have said!) So Pascal thought of another experiment.

He wanted the mercury barometer taken up a mountain where the air might be thinner. There, he predicted, less mercury would be held up than at the bottom of the mountain. He wrote to his brother-in-law, Monsieur Perrier, asking him to carry out the experiment and to be sure that there were people to watch it.

So, at 5.00am one fine September morning in 1648 Perrier sent out his servant to invite some important people to come. By 8.00am two clergymen, two lawyers and a doctor, Perrier, two barometer tubes, a bottle of the purest mercury, and a mule to carry it all, were ready at a monastery at the bottom of the mountain. Perrier set up one barometer and asked the monks to watch it carefully.

Then the rest set off to climb the 950 metre (3000ft) mountain. Perrier set up the second barometer at the top. To his delight this time the height of the mercury was 7cm less than at the bottom. Then they set off back down the mountain. Halfway down Perrier could not resist setting up

the barometer again. This time it was only 2.5 cm less than at the bottom.

Then they went back to the monastery and packed up the first barometer. Perrier was delighted, but he had an important question to ask the monks.

Evolution of the barometer

Now, was everyone convinced? It was a slow process. There were groups of people in almost every country who made barometers and used them to study the weather, or calculate the height of hills. Much later, when aeroplanes were invented, they carried small steel barometers to show how high they were flying. But the first person to use barometers to make weather forecasts was Otto Guericke, not a scientist at all but the mayor of the German city of Magdeburg.

QUESTIONS
1. Explain why a barometer can be used to indicate:
   a) the height above sea-level
   b) a change in the weather.
2. Water has a density of $1g/cm^3$. If the barometer liquid was turpentine (density $0.8g/cm^3$), how high do you think the liquid would rise in the tube?
3. Beer is traditionally pumped up from barrels in the cellar using a hand pump that requires air pressure to work. Explain why the cellar should not be more than 10 metres below the bar.
4. In Torricelli's times many people believed that the vacuum was sucking the mercury up the barometer. How would you have convinced them they were wrong?
5. Why did Perrier invite people to come with him up the mountain?
6. What question did Perrier ask the monks at the bottom of the mountain when they came there at the end of the day?
7. Find out about Otto Guericke and his studies into air pressure.

Let's build a cliff railway

> '*A tramway between the two towns of Lynton and Lynmouth ... the motive power being taken from the river Lyn ... put in tanks on rolling carriages and these let down the tramway under proper control. The weight of the water going down would, with the application of simple machinery bring up anything that might be desired from Lynmouth ... and visitors would find it a great benefit, for instead of climbing the hill, they could be drawn up in a comfortable carriage.*'

So read a letter to the *Lynton and Lynmouth Recorder* in December 1881. On Easter Monday 9 April 1890, the Cliff Railway was opened by the Lady of the Manor of Lynton. The coastguards fired a salute and bands played the National Anthem. Cheers greeted the first run. Since then, millions of people have travelled safely on the railway. There has never been an accident.

Where are Lynton and Lynmouth?

Lynton and Lynmouth are on the north coast of Devon, where Exmoor reaches the sea. Look at the sketch map. Lynmouth is a small fishing village with a harbour. Lynton is a small town of 1800 people built on a cliff top just above Lynmouth. Lynton and Lynmouth are very close but separated by a steep cliff 200 metres high. A very steep and bendy road links the two places. The West Lyn river and the East Lyn river join near Lynton and flow to the sea by Lynmouth harbour.

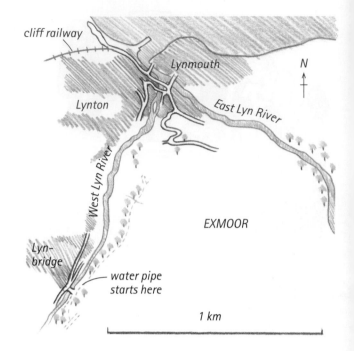

The north coast of Devon, around Lynmouth.

Designing the Cliff Railway

The Cliff Railway was designed by George Marks. His design was simple but clever. Two cars (or carriages) run on railway lines. The cars are linked by a single steel cable running around two pulley wheels of diameter 1.7 m. There are no engines or motors! The railway runs on water power! To understand how it works it may help to study Boxes 1 and 2.

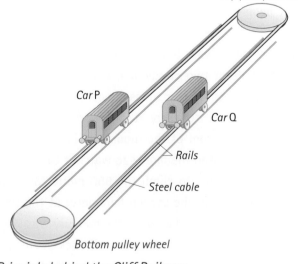

Principle behind the Cliff Railway.

BOX 1: BLOCKS HANGING FROM A PULLEY WHEEL

Two wooden blocks *P* and *Q* have the same weight. They are linked with a string over a pulley wheel. *P* and *Q* will stay in the same positions. The force of gravity pulling down on *P* is the same size as the force of gravity pulling down on *Q*. These two forces balance. We say that they are 'balanced forces'.

Now let's add another block *R* on the hook in the base of *P*. The force of gravity on *P* and *R* together will now be bigger than the force of gravity on *Q*. The two forces are unbalanced. Blocks *P* and *R* will fall and block *Q* will rise. But the blocks will not move at a steady speed up and down. Their speed will get greater and greater! We say that *P* and *R* accelerate downwards and block *Q* accelerates upwards.

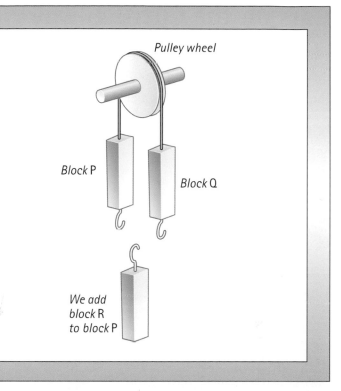

Pulley wheel

Block P

Block Q

We add block R *to block* P

BOX 2: BLOCKS ON A SLOPING CLIFF

Blocks *P* and *Q* are now on a steep slope like that of the Cliff Railway. They are held by a string over a pulley wheel. As in Box 1, the blocks will stay in the same positions. We now add another block *R* on to *P*. Blocks *P* and *R* together will move down the slope and block *Q* will move up the slope. But the acceleration of the blocks will be less than in Box 1. This time the blocks have to rub against the slope. They need an extra force to work against the forces of friction.

Friction is a force between two objects which 'tries to stop them moving against each other'. It is a force of friction between your shoes and the ground which stops you slipping when you walk. If you try to walk on a wet tiled floor or on ice you may slip because the force from friction will be very low.

Here, the blocks will only move if the force on *R* due to gravity is bigger than all the forces of friction on the blocks.

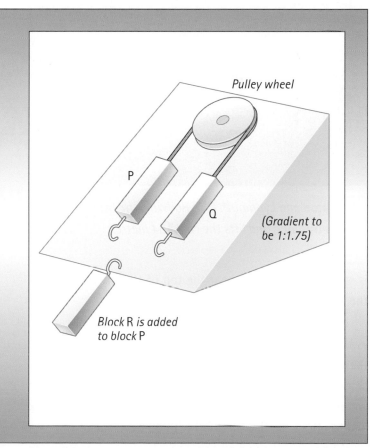

Pulley wheel

P

Q

(Gradient to be 1:1.75)

Block R *is added to block* P

Cars on the Cliff Railway

Look at the map and photos of the Cliff Railway. Water for the Cliff Railway comes in a pipe from the West Lyn River. The pipe is 1.4 km long and has a diameter of 12 cm. Water

The Lynton and Lynmouth Cliff Railway. The track is 265 metres long and lifts the cars 154 metres.

is stored in a reservoir near the top of the track. After use, the water runs back into the river.

Imagine that car *P* is at the top of the track and car *Q* is at the bottom. To make the cars move, car *P* must be heavier than car *Q*. This is done by pouring water into a big tank below the seats. The tank will hold 3200 litres or 3200 kg of water. This makes car *P* heavy enough to run down the track and to lift up car *Q*, even if full with 40 passengers.

When car *Q* reaches the top, its tank is filled with water. The water in car *P* is then emptied. Car *Q* then runs down the track and lifts up car *P*.

The tank of the top car being filled with water. It holds 3200 litres.

Acceleration, friction and control

If the Cliff Railway had been designed like this, it would have been very dangerous! As soon as water had filled the tank of car *P* with car *Q* empty, car *P* would have run down the track with a big acceleration, getting faster and faster, and hit the foot of the cliff with a bang. But if both cars had full tanks of water they would not move. Here's what happens.

The tanks of both cars are filled with water. Car *P* is at the top of the track and car *Q* is at the bottom. The drivers in both cars use the main brakes to clamp the cars to the rails. When all the passengers are on board, the brakes are taken off and water runs out of the tank below car *Q* until the cars begin to move. Without control, the cars would now accelerate but there is another special brake on each car.

The drivers use a special brake which presses down on the rails and lifts up one set of wheels on each car. This increases the force of friction between the cars and the rails. When forces of friction balance the forces of gravity, the cars run at a steady speed along the track.

Safety and the cars

A clever safety device called a 'governor' is linked to the wheels of each car. If the cars start to accelerate, the special brakes are pressed on.

The cars can only move if both drivers keep holding up a handle to stop the main brakes from working. If either driver lets go of their handle both cars will stop. The handle is known as the 'dead man's handle'. Similar brake handles are used on railway locomotives.

A car with its water tank below.

Lynton above Lynmouth, seen from the edge of Exmoor.

QUESTIONS

1. Read again Box 1: Blocks hanging from a pulley. Explain what we mean by 'balanced forces' for the blocks and pulley. On a very windy day we feel that we could be blown over by the wind. What do we do to stop being blown over? Use 'balanced forces' and 'friction' in your answer.

2. Read again the last paragraph of Box 2: Blocks on a sloping cliff. Why will the blocks only move if the force on *R* due to gravity is bigger than all the forces of friction? Why just the force on block *R*?

3. The Cliff Railway is powered by water. Describe what happens to the water from leaving the River Lyn until it is returned to the river at the bottom of the track. What kind of energy does the water give to the cars on the Cliff Railway?
   What kinds of energy do the cars have:
   a) at the top of the cliff?
   b) on the way down?

4. Both cars have the same mass when empty of passengers and water. Up to 3200 kg of water can be carried in each tank. With the tank in the top car full, 400 kg of water must be dropped from the tank in the bottom car to work against the forces of friction. This leaves 2800 kg of water to balance the weight of the passengers. Each passenger weighs 70 kg on average. If the top car is empty of passengers how many passengers can be lifted in the bottom car if all the water is dropped?

5. In 1952, the River Lyn flooded Lynton and Lynmouth. Over 22 cm of rain had fallen on Exmoor in 24 hours. Find out about this disaster in which many people were drowned.

3.12 It's not worth the risk

Do you travel by car to school or catch the bus? Do you play football after school or walk the dog? Eat a beefburger or fish and chips? Life is full of such decisions.

Can we be **sure** that we'll travel safely to school? We'll **probably** be safe from injury playing with the dog, won't we? Which foods are more **likely** to damage your health? The idea of probability plays a big part in our lives.

The table below shows the probability or risk of an adult dying in any one year from various causes:

Smoking 10 cigarettes a day	one in	200
All natural causes, age 40	one in	850
Any kind of violence or poisoning	one in	3300
Flu	one in	5000
Accident on the road	one in	8000
Leukemia	one in	12500
Playing soccer	one in	25000
Accident at home	one in	26000
Accident at work	one in	43000
Working in the radiation industry	one in	57000
Murder	one in	100000
Accident on railway	one in	500000
Hit by lightning	one in	10000000
Release of radiation from local power station	one in	10000000

(from *BMA Guide to living with risk*, Penguin, 1990)

In which of these activities is an adult most likely to die?

A very unlikely end!

The meaning of probability

These figures are based on past events. They are worked out from national statistics of causes of death gathered over many years. For example, in 1986 4900 people died on the road (0.8 per cent of the population) and 3832 people died from accidental falls (0.7 per cent of the population). These figures don't show that most people die from heart diseases or cancer. This table shows us the probability that we will die by being murdered. This is based on the number of murders in the past, compared with other deaths. It doesn't tell us how we will die!

The idea of probability is helpful in understanding scientific research. Many scientists try to understand how we are affected by what we eat and what we do. When we hear reports of scientific research, we might expect scientists to have definite answers – 100 per cent proof. This is just not possible.

Science in the news

Here are some headlines from reports of science research in *New Scientist* magazine. Notice that none of these headlines is definite. They all contain some uncertainty.

Let's look in a bit more detail at the last claim: babies who sleep with the lights on may be at greater risk of becoming short-sighted than those who sleep in the dark.

Notice the word 'may' – we need to look at how scientists did the work to decide whether we'll leave babies to sleep in the dark.

Richard Stone and other scientists at the University of Pennsylvania gave a questionnaire to parents of 479 children aged between 2 and 16. They asked whether their children slept with the light on, with a night-light or in darkness before the age of two. They chose the age of two because this is when the eye starts to grow rapidly. They then looked at how many of these children were now short-sighted.

WORLD'S END
There is one chance in 10 million that civilisation will end in 40 years' time, wiped out by a lump of rock one kilometre across.
(*New Scientist*, 29 May, 1999)

Healthy home
A huge study has failed to link fields created by household wiring to childhood cancers.
(*New Scientist*, 11 December, 1999)

Risky business
Don't put your daughter on the stage….she might get hurt. Today, on average, almost half the performers in each production in London's West End get work-related injuries.
(*New Scientist*, 7 November, 1998)

Lights out
Leave your kids in the dark and you may save their eyesight. (*New Scientist*, 15 May, 1999)

- 10 per cent of those who slept in darkness were short-sighted
- 55 per cent who slept with the light on were short-sighted
- 34 per cent of those who slept with a night-light were short-sighted.

These results need treating carefully. The scientists use the idea of probability to interpret the results. These results suggest it is more probable that if a baby sleeps with the light on he or she is found to be short-sighted later. But it does not tell us anything about how it happens or whether sleeping with the light on is a main cause of short sight. Richard Stone admits that 'We haven't proved cause and effect. A lot of work needs to be done.'

Further studies

Nearly a year later, there were two further studies about sleeping with the lights on. These were also reported in *New Scientist* (*Light Sleep*, 11 March 2000, p12). Karla Zadnik of Ohio State University did a study of the parents of 1220 children. Jane Gwiazda of the New England College of Optometry in Boston studied 213. Neither of these scientists found a link between sleeping with the lights on and short sight. Gwiazda suggests that short-sighted parents are more likely to leave the light on, perhaps because they need more light than people with better vision. Sight is partly determined by inheritance from parents. This may explain the findings in Richard Stone's study.

Cause and effect

Finding a link or correlation between two variables doesn't prove cause and effect. The other *New Scientist* reports

also use ideas of probability. Scientists collect evidence to help them make sense of their theories. They share results and ideas with other scientists so that theories can be developed further.

QUESTIONS

1. What would scientists have to do to be completely sure that sleeping with lights on makes you short-sighted? Why are we unlikely ever to get 100 per cent proof in this case?
2. Find other articles which report effects of our physical surroundings on us. Do newspaper articles always show how certain the claims are? Do they show who the scientists were who did the research and how they got their results?
3. For one of the other headlines, write an account of how the research might have been done. See if you can compare your account with the original *New Scientist* report.
4. Write a newspaper article of a science investigation you have done recently. Show what theories you used and how sure you can be of your conclusion.
5. The population of a large town is about 50 000. Work out how many people in this town are likely to die next year from the following causes:
   a) smoking
   b) flu
   c) playing soccer
   d) murder
   e) a railway accident.

Why are these numbers unlikely to be correct when death statistics for the town are collected next year?

Solar panels around the world

Solar cells change light energy into electrical energy. They do not 'run down' like cells and batteries which change chemical energy to electrical energy. Solar cells work best when the Sun shines on them. They do not work at all in the dark.

Most solar cells are made from the element silicon, which is found in sand. The silicon is made into a very pure crystal and cut into a thin slice. Minute amounts of different impurities are added to each side to make two slightly different forms of silicon. The side to face the Sun is made into 'n-silicon'. The lower side is made into 'p-silicon'.

Look at the diagram of a solar cell. The important part is where the two kinds of silicon meet. It is here that light energy causes an electric current to flow between the metal plates at the top and bottom.

Solar panels

A solar panel is a layer of solar cells. The bigger the area of the layer, the bigger will be the electric current generated in a circuit when light falls on the panel. Look at the photo of the solar panels on the roof of the Refuge on page 15 'Energy for living in the Alps'. There are 16 solar panels with a total area of 10 m². On a sunny day these panels give enough electric current to light a 300 watt electric lamp. This is the power of lamp which you could use to light a big room at home.

The first solar panel was made in 1954 in the USA by three scientists called Chaplin, Fuller and Pearsen working at the Bell Telephone Laboratories.

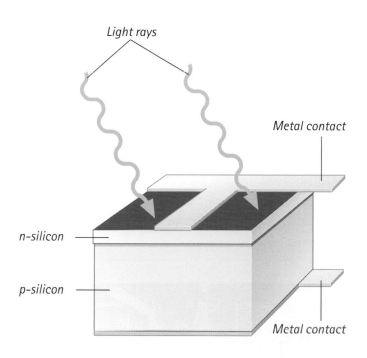

Structure of solar cells.

Energy from solar panels

When light from the Sun reaches Europe it gives a power of about 200 watts over one square metre on a sunny day. The power will be less on a cloudy day and zero, of course, at night.

But a solar panel with an area of 1 square metre will not give out 200 watts of electrical power. This is mainly because the solar cells can only use part of the Sun's light energy. Solar cells have an efficiency of about 15 per cent. This means that only 15 per cent of the power from the Sun is changed into electrical power. So a solar panel of area 1 square metre will only give a power of 30 watts (that is 200 x 15/100 = 30). This is only enough to light the kind of lamp used inside a fridge!

When are solar panels best used?
1. When other sources of electricity are difficult or impossible to reach.
2. When batteries using chemical substances cannot easily be charged.
3. When only small electric currents are needed.

Good things about solar panels
1. They change light energy directly into electric energy.
2. They last a long time as long as the surface is clean.
3. They don't have to be 'charged' like batteries, using chemicals which 'run down'.
4. They don't give out pollution, such as carbon dioxide or fumes, when they are working.
5. They don't use any fuel, such as oil, gas or coal, when they are working.

Bad things about solar panels
1. They don't work in the dark!
2. They give only a little electrical power on a dull day.
3. We need most energy in the winter, when many days are dull.
4. Large panels are needed to collect a lot of energy from sunlight.
5. Solar cells are expensive to make – they cost about £2 for each watt of electrical power.

1. These big solar panels are on a satellite moving around the Earth. This was one of the first uses of solar panels.

2. Can you see the small solar panel near the top right hand corner of this electronic calculator?

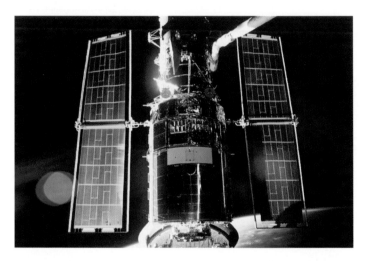

3. This solar panel is on the roof of a hut floating on a bed of reeds on Lake Titicaca in Peru. The solar panel is for a radio to link with people on shore.

4. This solar panel is on a big cattle ranch in Australia many miles from the nearest town. The panel is made to move to follow the Sun. Electric current is used to pump up water from below ground for cattle to drink.

5. This solar panel charges up a battery for a cattle fence. It is at 2000 m up in the French Alps. The battery and special electronics give a short burst of electric current around the fence. If the cattle try to cross the fence they get a mild electric shock.

6. This is a buoy at sea to warn ships of rocks. The solar panel powers a flashing light.

QUESTIONS

1. Why don't solar panels work in the dark?
2. Why do solar panels give more electric power on a sunny day than a cloudy day?
3. Explain why you think solar panels are used in the following places. Say why other sources of energy are difficult to use:
   a) Refuge de Longon (see Chapter 5 'Energy for living in the Alps')
   b) A satellite moving around the Earth in space
   c) On an island in Lake Titicaca in Peru
   d) An electronic calculator
   e) A cattle ranch in Australia
   f) An electric cattle fence in the Alps
   g) A buoy at sea
4. Try these calculations to work out how many electric fires can be run using a big solar panel.
   a) A big solar panel covers the area of a soccer pitch 120 m long and 80 m wide. The Sun is shining brightly.
      Area (A) of solar panel = length x width
      = _____ m²
   b) Power from the Sun (PS) = (A x S) = _____ watts

(Find S from the paragraph 'Energy from solar panels' on page 41)

   c) Electrical power (PE) from the solar panel
      = (PS x efficiency) = _____ watts
      Find the efficiency of a solar panel from the paragraph 'Energy from solar panels' on page 41
   d) Now calculate the number of 1 bar electric fires which could be powered by the solar panel. Each fire needs a power of 1000 watts.
      Number of fires = (PE/1000) = _____
   e) Just think of all this energy for free from the Sun! But how much would the solar panel cost? A solar panel to give 1 watt of power costs about £2. So the cost of the big solar panel would be (PE x 2) = £ _____
   f) What do you think about this cost? Do you think we should use big solar panels for our electricity supply? It would cost about £75 000 to buy the eletricity from the big solar panel in one year from our usual electricity supply. How many years would the big solar panel have to work to pay for itself? Now what do you think about the cost of the big solar panel?

Sound it out

> The frequency of a sound is the number of vibrations per second. 1 kHz (or 1 kilohertz) is one thousand vibrations per second hitting your eardrum.

SOUNDS	FREQUENCY
A dog whistle, bat and dolphin noises	Above 20 000 Hz
The highest note we can hear	20 000 Hz
Guitarist playing a very high note	10 000 Hz
Guitarist playing a high note	5000 Hz
Person singing a high note	1000 Hz
Person singing a low note	100 Hz
Bass drum in a rock band	20 Hz

You may think a mouse squeak is high-pitched but mice actually use even higher frequencies, called ultrasound, as well – even as high as 70 kHz – to communicate with each other. This may be why a cat is able to hear up to 90 kHz!

By comparison, the human ear is quite limited in what it can hear. The lowest notes are just a rumble at 30 Hz while a piercing 20 kHz is audible to young people. Sounds above that are called ultrasound. Most people find they are most sensitive to sounds between 1–4 kHz. This may be evolution's way of keeping us safe, as 1–4 kHz is just the pitch used by a mother shouting 'Watch out!'

Noise destroys

It's the highest frequencies which become inaudible when you suffer ear damage or as you get older. Loud noises will tire your sensitive hair cells in your inner ear and you might find your hearing is 'dulled' for a while after a concert or disco. Tinnitus (ringing in the ears) is another symptom, though scientists don't yet know what causes it.

Sound design

Graphic equalisers on stereo systems allow you to select how loud you want each frequency range to be and to try to recreate the 'concert experience'. In a conventional concert hall it's not just the direct sound from the front which is important. Reflections from the side walls, ceiling and back all make a difference. If there are too many reflections which carry on for too long (reverberation) then the sounds will blend and become 'muddy' and difficult to hear. On the other hand if the sound is not reflected much and is also absorbed by the furnishings or people then the effect is a 'dead' sound which appears flat. This would be ideal for speech but it's terrible for music. A human body absorbs sound as much as an open window. So when a sound check is carried out before the audience arrives, it is important that the upholstery on the seats absorbs the same amount of sound as when the hall is full of people.

Hearing double!

For outdoor concerts or very large venues bands often have sound stations at various places where speakers relay the sound to the audience at the back. As sound only travels a

A worker wearing ear defenders.

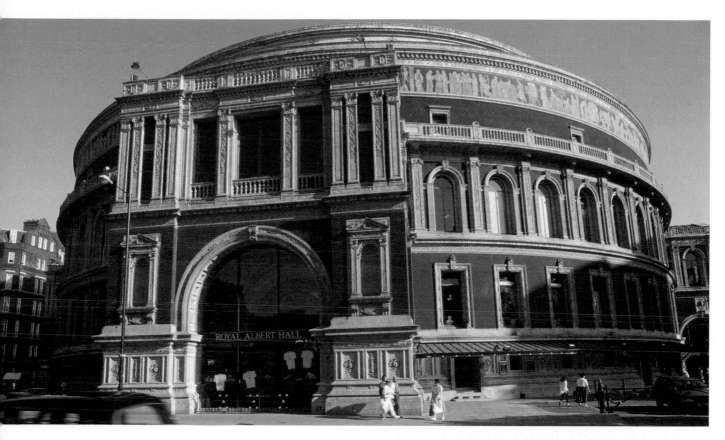

The Albert Hall in London is an excellent venue for concerts.

330 metres per second, there has to be an electronic delay on the speakers. This is so that they send out the sound at the same time as any sound from the front arrives. Otherwise the audience gets a very eerie and annoying effect of hearing everything twice, but fractions of a second apart. Unfortunately the sound won't match what you see on the giant screens.

High-frequency communication

But why should small mammals and insects use such high-pitched sounds? Obviously, if a creature communicates at higher frequencies than its predators can hear, that is an advantage – but cats obviously got wise to that!

It's also a matter of size. Smaller instruments – and insects – can make higher-pitched sounds because they can vibrate faster (higher frequency). Also, small mammals can only work out which direction a sound is coming from if it is high-pitched – because their ears are small and very close together (because their heads are small!).

Bats are well known for using ultrasound. The bat sends

Internal view of the Albert Hall.

Sound stations relaying sound to thousands of people at a concert.

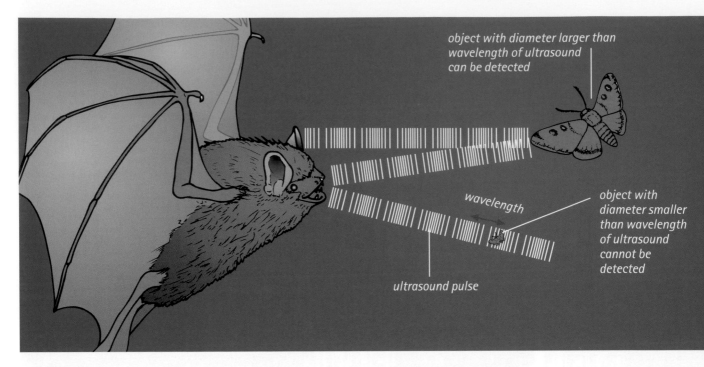

object with diameter larger than wavelength of ultrasound can be detected

object with diameter smaller than wavelength of ultrasound cannot be detected

wavelength

ultrasound pulse

The bat's squeak reflects off its prey and the bat can locate the insect.

out a very high-pitched squeak which is reflected off an obstacle or flying prey. The bat can hear the reflected sound (echo) and work out, from the time it took, where the object is. This is also how radar works on a ship, for example, but radar uses microwaves instead of ultrasound.

The Doppler effect

Bats can use another technique to spot the movement of prey. It's the same effect as a siren going past you at speed. As the ambulance approaches you hear a high note but when it has gone past you can notice the siren's note sounds lower. It is called the Doppler effect. When a bat, hanging on a tree, hears an echo which is higher-pitched than the sound it sent out, it knows something is coming towards it. A bigger change in pitch means the prey is approaching more quickly.

This is also the technique that police radar guns use to catch speeding motorists, except that they can calculate exactly what speed you are doing from how much the frequency has increased.

QUESTIONS

1. What are the lowest and highest frequencies that humans can hear?
2. What is ultrasound?
3. How does loud sound damage your hearing and what might be the first effects that you notice?
4. In a concert hall, what is reverberation?
5. If the reverberation time is too long or too short, why might the concert audience complain?
6. Draw a diagram to show why there has to be a delay on the sound sent out from the loudspeakers at great distances from the stage at outdoor concerts.
7. Why do small animals such as mice and bats use very high-pitched sounds?
8. How does radar on a ship work out where objects are?
9. Describe what the Doppler effect sounds like for a passing sound.
10. How does a radar gun used by the police work out how fast a car is moving?

From frisbees to spiral galaxies

I expect you know about frisbees. When you throw them with a flick of the wrist, they spin fast horizontally (round a vertical axis), and because they spin they remain horizontal. They don't turn over and over in somersaults. There is obviously something very stable about a spinning object.

The best way to test this out is to use a bicycle wheel. The easiest one to take off is the front wheel. Don't take the bolts and nuts off altogether. They will be useful. Now hold the wheel vertically with its axis horizontal in your hands, and get someone else to spin it fast.

- What do you feel?
- Can you turn the wheel over?
- Does it suddenly feel heavy, as if it had a mind of its own?

Now stop it from spinning and remind yourself how easy it can be to move when still.

Spin for stability

That is the sort of thing that convinces people that spinning

Taking off the front wheel of a bicycle.

The heavy, rotating bicycle wheel.

makes things stable. That means they keep on spinning in the same direction in space. In fact aeroplanes often use a spinning 'gyroscopic' compass. This is really only a heavy disc rotating on very good ball bearings in a bath of oil.

Aeroplanes often need to fly over the magnetic north pole, or very near it. Imagine what would happen if the pilot had to rely on a magnetic compass! Its needle would be attracted vertically downwards. But as the compass needle can only swing round horizontally it would get stuck. A gyroscopic compass would be much better. Once set spinning with its axis north–south it would keep its direction. This would be the only sort of compass that astronauts could use for space travel as well.

If you have a gyroscope of your own you can find out more about this stability. When you get good at using a gyroscope, it will 'balance' for you in all sorts of impossible positions. If you use the kind illustrated on the next page, for example, the gyroscope will begin to swing round. A child's spinning top will do the same.

Gyroscope Earth

In fact, the Earth itself might behave like a gyroscope, and that is why it has a true North Pole, not only a magnetic one. Our planet spins around an axis which points almost

A gyroscope.

exactly at Polaris, or the pole-star. This is conveniently to be found by the two pointers at the end of the Great Bear.

Has the spinning axis of the Earth always pointed at the pole-star since time began? The answer seems to be 'No'. At the time when the Ancient Egyptians built their pyramids they often included a shaft pointing upwards to the pole-star. This was so deep that a person standing at the bottom could see the pole-star even in broad daylight.

But the shaft does NOT point at the pole-star now. Just as the child's spinning top swings about, and the unbalanced gyroscope goes round in circles, so the axis of our Earth also 'precesses', as it is called. This means that, very, very slowly, Earth is swinging round a great circle which may take about 24 000 years to complete.

Spinning in the atmosphere

If we're thinking big, the best example of a spinning object that isn't solid is a spinning mass of air in the atmosphere. This is what cyclones and anticyclones are. In the northern hemisphere anticyclones are great discs of air spinning clockwise with high pressure inside them. Usually they bring dry weather with little wind. Wind from the outside cannot blow in because they have high pressure, and the spin keeps them fairly stable. Long hot dry spells in the summer are due to anticyclones.

Cyclones spin anticlockwise and have lower pressure

inside them than on the outside. They tend to be less stable than anticyclones, because winds blow in and fill in the low pressure.

Spinning in the oceans

A new discovery is of spinning currents of hot water in the deep oceans. These rise out of underwater volcanoes when they erupt. They are not only pretty stable but they may contain small living creatures. It has long been a puzzle to scientists how sea-creatures from one volcanic vent, seem to land up at another 150 kilometres or more away. The distances are much too far for them to swim through the cold deep water in between. A young American physicist worked out a model for the spinning disc of warm water. This predicted that once it reached a size of two kilometres across and 200 metres thick, it could be stable spinning in the daily rotation of the Earth. On a smaller scale these spinning 'lenses' of water would be stable at different speeds and different sizes. The scientist decided to mount a fish tank rotating on a flat turntable and they used coloured dyes to search for spinning vortices. The scientists found them, just as they had predicted.

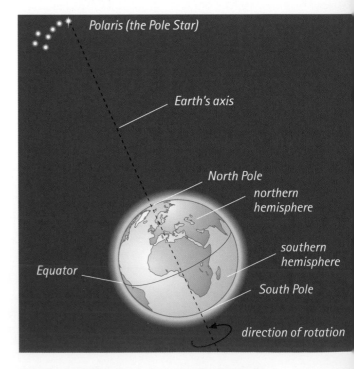

The spinning Earth pointing to the North Star.

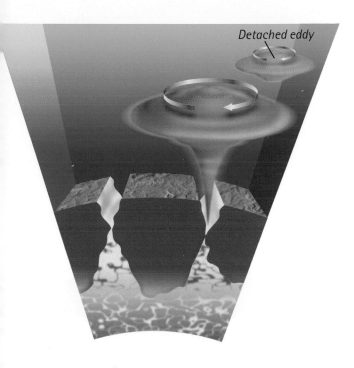

Whirls in the sea, carrying life.

A slowly swirling spiral galaxy.

Two women biologists then teamed up with the physicists to find out if the tiny young 'fry' of fish from the deep hot water in the ocean could live inside the slowly spinning vortices. They said that they were like 'passengers in a hot air balloon'. (It also sounds like extraterrestrials in a UFO!)

The ultimate in spinning

The last problem to do with spinning vortices is about the great spiral galaxies of the Universe. You may know that most galaxies spin, but not in closed discs. Our own galaxy, the Milky Way, is a spiral galaxy with five arms, as many of them have. No one yet knows quite why galaxies are this shape, and they certainly do not know why they should be stable. Like the firework called a Catherine Wheel, a spiral galaxy should shoot off hot matter as it revolves, and so get smaller and smaller. If it did, then it would accelerate and spin even faster, and so die out even more quickly! They would certainly NOT be stable. And yet we can 'see' spiral galaxies spinning slowly round far away from us, almost up to the observable edge of the Universe. So how do they do it?

This is still a mystery. Could it be invisible 'black matter' pressing in on the rotating galaxy and keeping it all together? Or could it be the even more mysterious 'black

energy' which no one yet really understands. Help! we need some good physicists to solve this new problem.

QUESTIONS

1. If spinning makes things stable, give TWO examples where things balance because something is spinning, and would fall over otherwise.

2. It has long been known that the Earth is slightly flattened at the two poles. Scientists think this happened while the Earth was still hot and molten. Explain what may have happened.

3. In the science fiction story *Ringworld* space travellers reach an inhabited world which has been engineered and inhabited by intelligent life. It is a giant rotating ring which is stable, and it has air and a kind of gravity inside the ring because it is rotating. This provides a long walk inside the whole Ringworld, ending up where you started. Draw a diagram of this walk indicating the direction of gravity and what the view out of a window might look like.

Strange rays in Wurzburg

The following extracts are taken from the diary of Charles Nootnangle, written in 1895. Nootnangle was a student of Wilhelm Conrad Roentgen, the discoverer of X-rays, at his laboratory in Wurzburg, Germany.

The value of Roentgen's discovery was quickly spotted. By the following year army doctors were locating bullets in wounded soldiers and on 8 February 1896, Edwin Frost in America produced the first X-ray image of a fractured bone.

Wilhelm Conrad Roentgen.

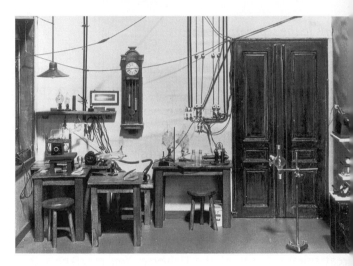

Roentgen's laboratory in Wurzburg.

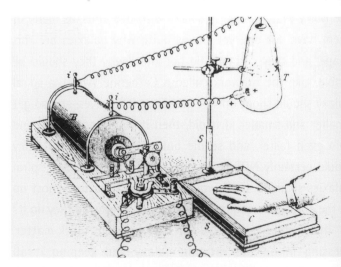

Roentgen's apparatus with the Crooke's tube top right.

Thursday October 31st 1895

Roentgen is clearly agitated and excited today. He feels that there is a discovery around the corner. I have been employed checking that his precious Crookes tubes are working. I hate the device. It is a glass tube with two metal plates inside connected to wires outside. The whole beastly thing has to have as much air pumped out as possible before the opening in the glass is sealed with a bunsen burner. My fingers are sore from the burns I have got from the glass. And now he tells me that the air has leaked back in to the two best tubes through tiny cracks in the glass. I'll be here until late tonight sealing and checking them. And I had so hoped to get to the concert in Spiegelplatz this evening.

Friday November 1st 1895

Roentgen is planning new tests on the cathode rays that the tubes produce. The thing works by applying a very large voltage across the plates. Thousands of volts. So this large voltage causes a current to flow in the tube from the negative plate to the positive. Roentgen wants to investigate the invisible rays that escape from the tube and make a specially coated paper give off a green light. This glow is called fluorescence. I think Roentgen's idea is to see what these rays will pass through.

Tuesday November 5th 1895

Mercifully the vacuum in the tubes is holding well. But today he has got me checking all the curtains in the laboratory. It is vital to have total darkness, he says, to ensure that he can see even the smallest glow of fluorescence.

Thursday November 7th 1895

My last job for the great experiment – which he will not reveal to me. I must finish today as I am off to Heidelburg this evening to visit my delightful Amelia for the weekend.

I have merely to coat a pile of sheets of paper with the chemical that makes it fluoresce. Only three more sheets to paint and I am done.

There, that is the last of them. At last I can get out of this lab which, with the windows all covered, is now hot and smells of the fluorescent chemicals I have been using. Fresh air and Amelia. Heaven! Let me but write the first letter of her name on this spare piece of paper that I have found. So my love for her is written invisibly on this sheet now only to be revealed by the energies of invisible rays.

Monday November 11th 1895

No sooner am I in through the door than Roentgen grabs me. I know the look in his eyes. It is the thrill I have seen in him when he has made a breakthrough. He pulls me into the lab. I see that the Crookes tube is set up and connected to the electrical supply. Speechless, he switches on and holds the fluorescent paper a few centimetres beyond the tube. It emits the greenish glow that I have become so familiar with. No cause for excitement surely. We know that the cathode rays can pass this far through the air to create their effect. And indeed, as Roentgen moves the paper away from the tube the glow fades as the cathode rays can no longer reach the paper.

I look at Roentgen puzzled. Without words he goes to the power supply and turns the voltage up, meanwhile pointing to the corner of the lab. It is dark. Suddenly I see a green glow begin to appear. But this cannot be. The spot is 3 metres from the Crookes tube. No cathode ray can reach that far. Then I make out the pattern of the glow. It is my discarded love note from last Thursday and what is glowing is the 'A' that I painted there. Roentgen tells me that he was at work late on Friday night when he saw the glowing 'A' appear. He explains that the distance is too great for cathode rays to be responsible. This effect must be the result of other invisible rays. At a loss as to what to call them he settles on X-rays.

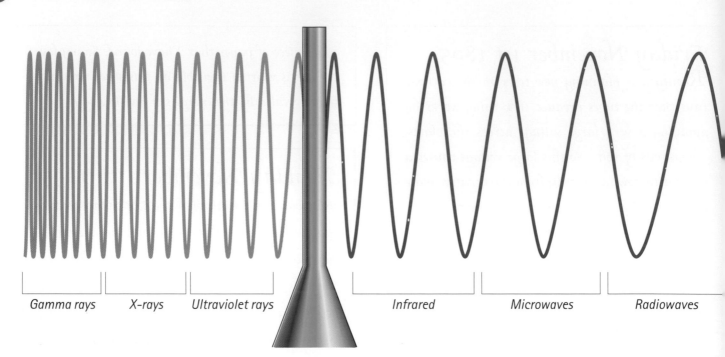

We know that Roentgen's X-rays were just like a very short wavelength version of visible light.

Friday 15th November 1895

I have never experienced such a busy week. I have been caught up in the excitement of this new discovery and feel delighted that my love for my darling Amelia should have played a small part in this historic event.

Roentgen and I have been furiously investigating the properties of these new X-rays. He is like a man possessed. He wishes to have his first thoughts ready to present to the Wurzburg Physical and Medical Society before the New Year. We have constructed a large chamber perhaps 3 metres tall and 1.5 metres square made of zinc and lead. The Crookes tube is positioned to send its mysterious X-rays into the chamber through an aluminium plate, which will cut out the cathode rays. Inside the chamber we have spent all week placing different materials in front of our fluorescent paper to test the rays' penetrating power.

A pack of cards has no effect and blocks of wood appear transparent too. Aluminium does seem to enfeeble the rays somewhat, but only lead or glass plates made of flint glass seem able to resist the passage of these rays significantly.

We are in no doubt that these rays will find quick application. I brought my hunting rifle in yesterday. In the image I could clearly see the cartridges inside and also cracks and faults in the metal barrel invisible to the naked eye. On Tuesday Roentgen persuaded Bertha, his wife, to place her hand for 30 minutes in front of a photographic plate and he now proudly shows the image of her bones within the flesh along with the sharp outline of her wedding ring on the fourth finger.

Amelia arrives this evening. I intend to show her this image of Bertha's hand to warm her to the proposal I intend to make her.

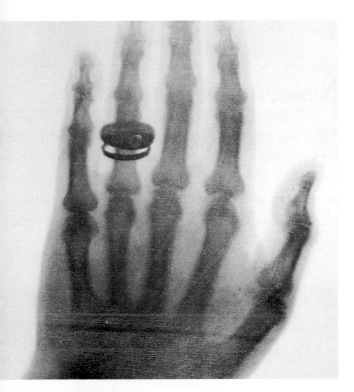

X-ray of Bertha's hand.

X-rays can detect cracks and faults in metal objects.

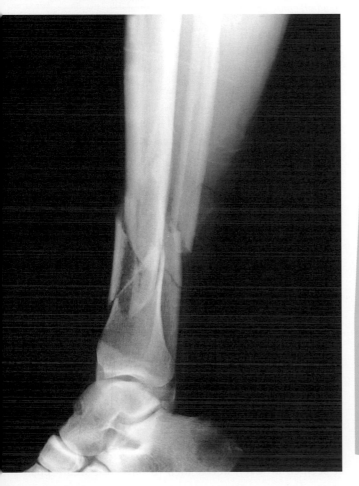

X-ray of a broken leg.

QUESTIONS

1. Put these materials in order according to how well they absorb X-rays, with the one that absorbs least X-rays first:

   Aluminium   Wood   Lead

2. Find out how flint glass is made. Why do you think it is better than normal glass at blocking X-rays?

3. We now know that the cathode rays that Crookes discovered and that Roentgen was investigating are tiny particles called electrons. Try to find out more about electrons and why they cannot travel very far in air.

4. Roentgen's experiment produced X-rays by firing electrons against the glass at the end of the tube. What did he do that Crookes had not done to make his tube produce the X-rays?

5. In some ways Roentgen was lucky to discover X-rays. He spotted something he was not looking for. Do you think this happens often in scientific research? Can you think of any other examples? (Clue: Find out about the discovery of penicillin.)

6. You may well have had an X-ray picture taken by your dentist. He or she will have put a plastic-covered shield into your mouth. What job do you think this does and what material do you think you might find inside the shield?

7. X-rays are very useful to us, but they can also be dangerous. A lot of the early experimenters ended up with deformed hands. Try to find out how X-rays can harm us and what people who work in hospital do to protect themselves.

The steam engine, the telegraph and the murderer

You probably know the story about how the steam engine was developed. It all began, curiously enough, with improvements in our understanding of atmospheric pressure (see page 31 'Taking a barometer up the mountain'). Scientists began to realise that if you could have any sort of tube or flask with very little air inside it, the atmosphere pushing on the outside might make it collapse. As you can see in the diagrams below, if water is boiled in a can, closed up, then left to cool down, the atmospheric pressure outside the can will crush it flat.

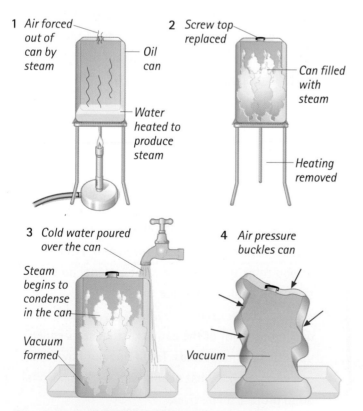

1 Air forced out of can by steam — Oil can — Water heated to produce steam

2 Screw top replaced — Can filled with steam — Heating removed

3 Cold water poured over the can — Steam begins to condense in the can — Vacuum formed

4 Air pressure buckles can — Vacuum

The pressure of the atmosphere crushes a can.

Newcomen's engine

Then came the idea of letting steam into a cylinder, where it pushes out a piston, which prevents the entry of more steam, and then cooling it down with a squirt of cold water, which then allows the pressure of the atmosphere to push the piston back. If this is made to happen over and over again the piston will go in and out.

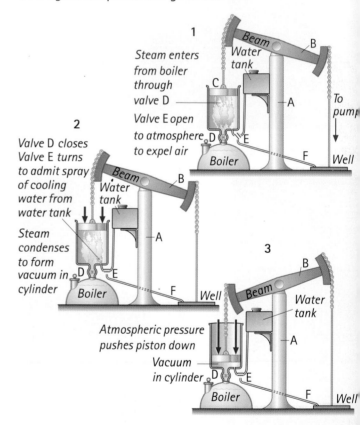

1 Steam enters from boiler through valve D — Valve E open to atmosphere to expel air — Beam — Water tank — B — C — A — To pump — D — E — Boiler — F — Well

2 Valve D closes Valve E turns to admit spray of cooling water from water tank — Steam condenses to form vacuum in cylinder — Beam — B — Water tank — A — D — E — Boiler — F — Well

3 Atmospheric pressure pushes piston down — Vacuum in cylinder — Beam — B — Water tank — A — D — E — Boiler — F — Well

Steam pushes up the piston, then a spray of cold water is released and atmospheric pressure pushes the piston down.

It was a terrible waste of fuel to keep on squirting cold water right into the hot cylinder, and then heating it all up again with more steam. Fortunately, James Watt had a better idea.

Watt's engine

It seemed an even better idea to have the steam push the piston in from one side and then back again from the other

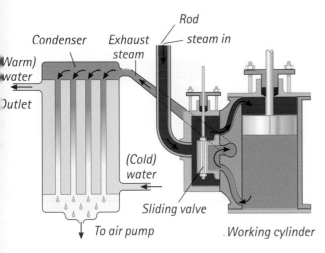

Condenser
Exhaust steam
Rod
steam in
(Warm) water
Outlet
(Cold) water
Sliding valve
To air pump
Working cylinder

James Watt's steam engine.

That way it did not have to be cooled down. If you look carefully at the diagram above, you will see the sliding valve that the steam comes through – it automatically lets the steam in on one side of the piston and then in through the other side.

The first locomotives

All the engineers had to do now was to get this steam power to turn the wheels of a vehicle. The first 'locomotive engines' of this kind were heavy and slow moving. Gradually they improved and by 1830 George Stephenson built his 'Rocket' locomotive engine, which pulled trains of three or more carriages from Liverpool to Manchester, on a regular timetable, with first, second and third class carriages.

Everyone was very concerned with safety because on the very first trial run a man had been killed. It seemed at that time that a speed of forty miles an hour was dangerously fast. What would happen if the train came off the lines? Worse still, could the driver stop in time if the train came round the corner and there was a fallen tree right across the lines? There were no telephones, mobile or otherwise in those days. Sometimes a person would have to leap on a horse and gallop as fast as they could to wave to the train driver so that he would put on his brakes. Unfortunately, they did not often get there in time and there were many accidents.

How could you send really fast messages? In the old days, messages were sent by lighting bonfires (beacons) on the top of hills. That would be no good for trains which ran in deep cuttings, under bridges, and even through tunnels. Their drivers would not be able to see the light from the beacons.

Electric messages

By the end of the eighteenth century people had already begun to think about electricity for carrying messages. At first there were no good batteries so the only idea was to send discharges of electricity down a long insulated wire from an electrostatic machine. The patent for this machine suggested that the receiver held the bare end of the wire in his hands, and just waited until he got a shock!

The railway engineers designed and built hand-worked signals. The handle pulled a wire, and then the arm of the signal either went up (for stop) or went down (for go). The train could be stopped by the signal man. But still no messages could be sent, except STOP or GO.

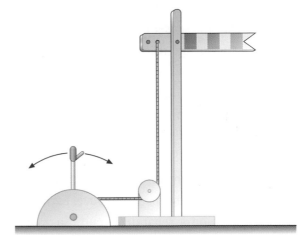

An early STOP / GO mechanical railway signal.

Electricity's magnetic effect

Then the electric battery was invented. Once scientists had this source of safe electricity they found out a lot of things that electric current could do when it flowed around a circuit. One of these was that electric current had a magnetic effect. Even if it only flowed down a straight wire it could affect a compass needle held above or below the wire, by a little bit. Then they found out that if the wire was wound into a coil, when the current flowed it had a much stronger magnetic effect. This suggested to someone with an inventive mind

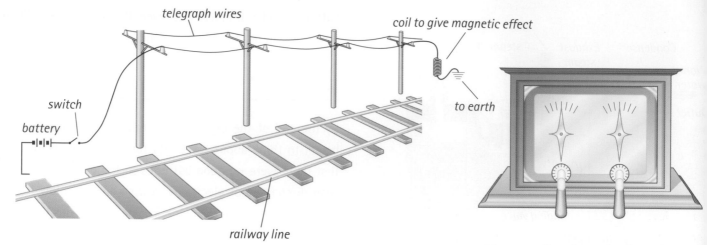

Principle behind the electric telegraph.

A two-needle telegraph allows the sender to transmit messages.

that the magnetic pull of the coil would be able to move a lever, just so long as the circuit had no gaps in it.

Thinking about this, the inventors decided to 'earth' the circuit so that, because soil is moist, it would make a complete circuit and the current would flow whenever messages were sent. The sender needed a switch to turn the current on and off. But the receiver at the other end also needed to de-code the message in some way so that the movements of the lever could make sense. It's not much good receiving a message if you don't know what it means!

On one of the early railway lines from the south coast to London, going through Slough on the way, the receiver at Paddington station in London had 'a two-needle telegraph' like the one in the diagram above. Each of these needles was worked on a separate circuit. So you could have one needle moving, or two. That made it possible to make a code, rather like the Morse code with dots and dashes, so that the sender could spell out the message. The receiver at Paddington had to write down the code:

.... 2,2, 2,1, 1,1,1,2, 1,2 etc.

Then they could look up in their code-breaking book and find out what it meant.

Murder!

One day during 1845 a man who lived in Slough killed his wife and leapt on the London train to get away from the scene of the crime. He relaxed once the train moved off. He was sure that no one could reach him now. No policeman could travel as

fast as a train! What he did not know was that a message about the murder had been sent to the stationmaster in Slough and that he had sent it on by the new electric telegraph, to London Paddington. So when he got off the train there were three policemen waiting to arrest him for the murder of his wife. The murderer was astonished! All the London evening newspapers carried the story. You might say that the heroes of the day were the inventors of the steam engine and of the telegraph!

Questions

1. Describe how a vacuum is formed in the 'collapsing can experiment'. How else could a vacuum have been produced in the can?

2. In the Newcomen steam engine, cold water is squirted into the cylinder so the steam will condense. Why does this cause the piston to travel downwards?

3. Explain why the sliding valve system in Watt's engine is more efficient.

4. How could you use:
   - a battery
   - an iron screw
   - some wire
   - a lamp
   - a wooden signal
   to make a circuit which would turn on a red light and raise the lever arm at the same time when a train was approaching? Sketch your design.

A central Sun

Hello. My name is Thomas Recorde. The year is 1687 and I am an old man of 86, very close to death. My eyesight is failing me but by my bed is a wonderful book just written by a young man from Cambridge University. His name is Isaac Newton and his book, called the *Principia*, describes the laws that govern the whole Universe. He talks of a strange force called 'gravity', which pulls apples to the ground and holds the planets in their orbits. Everyone is cheering this book and full of excitement about its explanation for the way heavenly bodies move. They praise his ideas as if they were new. But Newton himself says he is only standing on the shoulders of giants. I know he is right. I know who one of those giants was. My grandfather told me about him 78 years ago.

Only known image of Robert Recorde.

Astronomer grandfather

I was 8 years old. My younger brother was being born and I was sent from London to St Albans to stay with my grandparents. My grandfather, Robert Recorde, was a physician in the town and a keen astronomer. One night I was missing my mother and could not sleep so I was gazing out of the window at a clear sky, filled with stars. My grandfather came in. 'What do you see up there, Tommy?', he asked. 'Twinkling stars', I replied. 'More stars than there are grains of sand on a beach.'

My grandfather smiled and sat down beside me. He began to point out the patterns in the stars and gave them names. Then he told me that there were what he called wandering stars. These were not really stars at all but planets. He pointed to one that looked quite red. Then he suggested that, if I wasn't tired, I might like to learn some astronomy. He told me to fix up a square on the window and to draw the pattern of stars I could see through it. It took me a long time, but by the time I had finished I knew the patterns well. Tired, I went to sleep.

I was roused from this sleep by my grandfather shaking me. It was still dark and I looked anxiously at my grandfather but he led me silently to my former position by the window and gestured for me to look again through the square. Amazed, I saw that the pattern through the square was not as before. Looking more carefully, I saw that the main pattern of stars that I had drawn was still there but was now some distance to the right of the square but, even more amazingly, the reddish wandering star had moved even further and was quite close to the horizon now.

'What do you make of that?', he asked.

'Well', I said, 'it seems that the stars revolve around us at night as the Sun does by day.'

A Sun-centred Universe?

Grandfather smiled and looked me in the eye intently. Then he grabbed my arm, picked up a huge sack from a cupboard and led me out to the field behind the house. Here he pulled hundreds of candles from the sack. One candle was very large, the sort they use in churches. This he lit and placed in the centre of the field. The others he arranged in

57

patterns a long way away at the edges of the field and lit these too. Then he told me to walk in a circle around the large candle. I started to walk and, as I did so, he took me by the shoulders and made me spin as I walked.

'What do you see?', he shouted, excitedly.

I described the way the bright central light was only visible for half the time and blinded me to the other candles but that, when I had my back to the big candle I could see the patterns of the other candles moving across my vision. My grandfather clapped his hands excitedly and pulled out a ball of red wool which glinted in the light of the central candle as he held it up. He started walking in a circle with it, just a bit further out than me. 'Nicolaus, you were right', he shouted madly. But at that point two things brought our wild game to an end. My grandmother leant out of the window and told him she would leave him if he indulged this foolishness one more time when people were trying to sleep and I collapsed to the ground in a dizzy whirl.

Copernicus or Ptolemy?

That afternoon, my grandfather took me for a walk and tried to explain. As a young man, in the 1540s, he had worked as royal physician to Queen Mary. At this time he had started to hear from European travellers to the Court of a bold new book written by a Polish canon called Nicolaus Copernicu called *Concerning the Revolution of the Heavenly Sphere* and published in 1543, the year Copernicus died. This boo argued that the Greeks, whose ideas on astronomy were jus being discovered, had got things wrong. In particula Copernicus disagreed with the famous Greek astronome Ptolemy, who had made careful drawings and calculations t show how the Sun and all the planets orbit around th Earth. My grandfather explained that, although Ptolemy' model just about worked, it was very complicated an involved the planets travelling in epicycles (orbits aroun orbits). Copernicus' book showed that the system could b made much simpler by putting the Sun at the centre an having every other planet, including ours, orbit around it.

My grandfather had got hold of a copy of Copernicus book and was persuaded by the mathematical argument for a Sun-centred system. He had immediately set to tryin to persuade the universities to stop teaching Ptolemy' system and to adopt the Copernican system instead. Bu very quickly he had found himself in dispute with th church. The priests argued that the Bible talks of the Su moving through the heavens. They also insisted that, a humans made in God's image, we must inhabit a planet a the centre of the Universe. In addition, the scholars argue that if the Earth travelled around the Sun we should surel

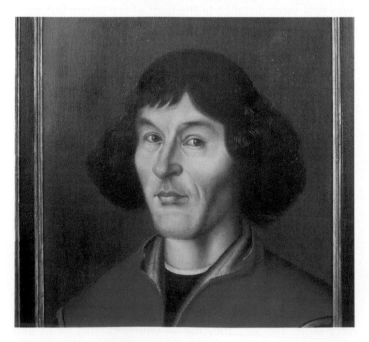

Nicolaus Copernicus.

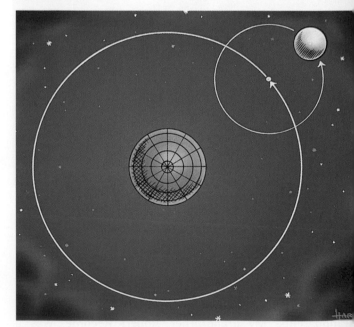

A planet travelling in an epicycle.

Complicated models were created to show the movement of the planets.

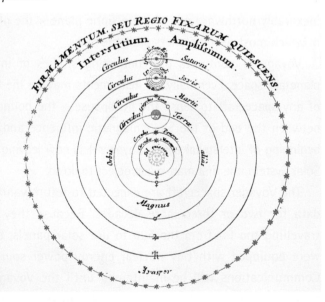

The Sun-centred system.

...ly off it. My grandfather did not have the time to fight such powerful opponents and so he contented himself with writing a book in 1556 called *The Castle of Knowledge* in which he defended Copernicus' theory.

Kepler enters the argument

In the same year that my grandfather explained the Copernican system to me a man called Johannes Kepler published some very powerful measurements of the movements of the planets and stars which supported the Sun-centred theory. Then, 20 years after my grandfather's death, an Italian called Galileo published a book which also defended Copernicus' system. Galileo was put under house arrest by the Catholic Church for the rest of his life for his ideas so I suppose my grandfather had a lucky escape.

But gradually, during my lifetime, I have seen the great idea of Copernicus being accepted. And now, as I lie here 144 years after Copernicus published his ideas, Isaac Newton finally seems to have won the battle. For my grandfather's memory and for his beliefs I can now publicly shout these final words of mine on Earth:

'Nicolaus, you were right!'

QUESTIONS

1. Why do we seem to see the Sun orbiting around us?
2. How long does the Earth take to turn on its own axis and how long does it take to orbit the Sun?
3. Draw a diagram to show the order of the planets orbiting the Sun.
4. Which planet did grandfather's ball of red wool represent?
5. Imagine you lived in 1580 and had read Copernicus' work. Do you think you would have believed him? Give two reasons for your decision.
6. One of the arguments made against Copernicus was that, if the Earth was orbiting the Sun, we would see the stars from a different angle from either end of the orbit. But we don't. Can you think why not?
7. Find out something about one other model of the Universe that people used to believe. Why do you think it was so hard for astronomers to work out how the Universe operates?

Voyager

The twin spacecraft Voyager 1 and Voyager 2 were launched by NASA in 1977 from Cape Canaveral, Florida. The Voyagers were to fly past Jupiter and Saturn, Saturn's rings, and the larger moons of the two planets. They were to take the first close up pictures and measurements. As the mission went on, additional fly-bys of the two outermost giant planets, Uranus and Neptune, proved possible.

As the spacecraft flew across the solar system NASA reprogrammed them to give the Voyagers greater capabilities than they possessed when they left the Earth. Their two-planet mission became four. Their five-year lifetimes stretched to 12 and more. Between them, Voyagers 1 and 2 would explore all the giant outer planets of our solar system, 48 of their moons, and the unique systems of rings those planets possess. The Jupiter and Saturn fly-past alone provided enough material to rewrite astronomy textbooks.

There was a rare arrangement of the outer planets in the late 1970s. This allowed for a four-planet mission in the minimum of time. This layout of Jupiter, Saturn, Uranus and Neptune occurs only once every 175 years.

Launch of the first Voyager.

Voyager 1's trajectory was designed to send the spacecraft closely past the large moon Titan and behind Saturn's rings. Then the path bent the spacecraft's flight inexorably northward out of the ecliptic plane – the plane in which most of the planets orbit the Sun.

Voyager 1 continues on, conducting studies of interplanetary space. Eventually, its instruments may be the first of any spacecraft to sense the heliopause – the boundary between the end of the Sun's magnetic influence and the beginning of interstellar space. Voyager 1 is now leaving the Solar System, the first man-made object to do so.

The Voyager spacecraft are expected to return valuable data for two or three more decades. Because they are travelling too far from the Sun to use solar panels, they were equipped with tiny nuclear energy power sources. Communications will be maintained until the Voyagers' power sources can no longer supply enough electrical energy.

Each probe is equipped with instruments to conduct 10 different experiments. The instruments include television cameras, infrared and ultraviolet sensors. In addition, each spacecraft's radio is being used to conduct experiments.

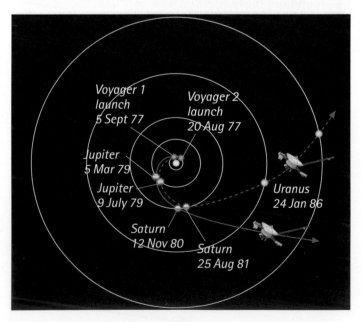

Voyager 1
launch
5 Sept 77

Voyager 2
launch
20 Aug 77

Jupiter
5 Mar 79

Jupiter
9 July 79

Uranus
24 Jan 86

Saturn
12 Nov 80

Saturn
25 Aug 81

Flight paths of Voyagers 1 and 2.

FACTFILE: JUPITER

Jupiter is the largest planet in the Solar System, and is composed mainly of hydrogen and helium, with small amounts of methane, ammonia and water vapour. Colourful bands and atmospheric clouds and storm demonstrate Jupiter's vast weather system, and the giant planet is now known to possess 16 moons.

Jupiter.
The Great Red Spot was revealed to be a complex storm. An array of other smaller storms and eddies have been found throughout the dense clouds of Jupiter's atmophere.

The Great Red Spot.

The discovery of active volcanoes on the moon Io was easily the greatest unexpected discovery at Jupiter. It was the first time these had been seen on another body in the Solar System. The Voyagers observed the eruption of nine volcanoes on Io. Smoke plumes from the volcanoes extend to more than 300 kilometres (190 miles) above the surface.

Jupiter's moon Europa is the most likely other place we know in the Solar System that could support life, like on Earth. Europa is thought to have a thin crust (less than 30 kilometres or 18 miles thick) of water ice, possibly floating on a 50-kilometre-deep (30-mile) ocean. It is in this ocean, insulated from the cold of space, where life might develop.

The rings around Jupiter.
Voyager found a faint, dusty ring of material around Jupiter. Its outer edge is 129 000 kilometres (80 000 miles) from the centre of the planet. Io acts as an electrical generator as it moves through Jupiter's magnetic field, developing 400 000 volts across its diameter and generating an electric current of 3 million amps.

FACTFILE: URANUS

Uranus is the third largest planet in the Solar System. Uranus is distinguished by the fact that it is tipped on its side. This probably happened in a collision with a planet-sized body early in the Solar System's history. The average temperature is about -210°C.

Voyager found 10 new moons, bringing the total number to 15.

Uranus and some of its moons.

FACTFILE: SATURN

Saturn is the second largest planet in the Solar System. Saturn is known to have at least 17 moons and a complex ring system. Like Jupiter, Saturn is mostly hydrogen and helium. Its hazy yellow hue was found to be marked by broad atmospheric banding similar to those found on Jupiter. Voyager found the greatest surprises in Saturn's rings. It is thought that these rings formed from larger moons that were shattered by impacts of comets and meteors. The resulting particles range from dust to boulder to house-size.

Saturn and its rings.

FACTFILE: NEPTUNE

This planet was at that time the most distant member of the Solar System from the Sun. (Pluto has since once again become most distant.)

Neptune.

Neptune is now known to have eight moons, six of which were found by Voyager. The strongest winds on any planet were measured on Neptune. Most of the winds there blow westward, or opposite to the rotation of the planet at up to 2000 kilometres (1200 miles) an hour.

Triton, the largest of the moons of Neptune is one of the most interesting objects in all the Solar System.

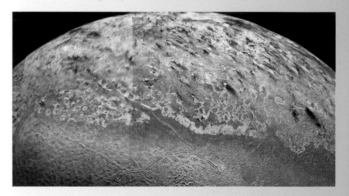

Triton.

Triton's high density shows it is a captured object and not a true moon. It has been orbiting Neptune for as long as one billion years, but before that Triton was probably another planetary member of our Solar System.

QUESTIONS

1. Why are the four outer planets called 'gas giants'?
2. How do the Voyager spacecraft make electricity?
3. What information about the planets can the Voyager spacecraft send back to Earth?
4. All these outer planets have moons. Describe what the moons are like. Are they made of gas, like the planets?
5. What is the weather like on Jupiter?
6. What are Saturn's rings made of?
7. What happened to tip Uranus on its side?
8. What is special about Triton, which is one of Neptune's moons?

Reflecting on light

Animals were using 'bio-reflectors' – living cells or substances produced by them that reflect light – long before humankind worked out how to make mirrors from shiny metal surfaces. Light reflected from a cat's eyes at night and the brightness of birds' plumage and butterflies' wings all make use of bio-reflectors. But, although bio-reflectors may look metallic, they are really made of stacks of thin, transparent films.

The butterfly's metallic shine is really caused by thin transparent layers reflecting blue light.

The reflections from a cat's eyes at night inspired a scientist to invent the 'Cats' eyes' in the middle of the road.

Multiple mirrors

When light hits the first layer of film, some of it is reflected back while the rest travels into the film. When this light hits the back of the film it, too, is reflected and adds to the light that was reflected from the front. This gives a much brighter reflection than you would get from a single layer of film. With five or ten layers stacked together the bio-reflector can be better than a normal silvered mirror. And one more trick that Nature has up her sleeve: if a film is exactly the right thickness it will let all but one colour of light pass through and reflect only that one colour.

Laser magic

But humankind has now gone one better than the animal world. We don't only use reflections for checking how we look in a mirror or to increase the brightness, say, of a car's headlights. Compact discs use reflections of laser light from the surface of the disc as a code for the music we hear or for the computer games we play.

However hard you look at the surface of a CD you will not be able to see the millions of microscopic pits and bumps in its metal surface. Yet these are essential if the CD is to work. The disc has a spiral pattern of bumps and the

The CD is designed to reflect light with perfect precision.

Electron micrograph of scales from the wing of a butterfly.

Barcodes reflect light from the white lines, but not the black.

laser inside the CD player reflects off them as it scans over the disc. If the laser light is reflected off a 'bump', the sensor inside the CD player receives it and registers a '1'. But if no light is reflected because it has hit a 'pit', then the sensor receives no light and registers a '0'. The ones and zeros are binary code (sometimes called digital information) for the musical sounds or computer game, which is then decoded by the electronic circuits in the machine to re-create what we see or hear.

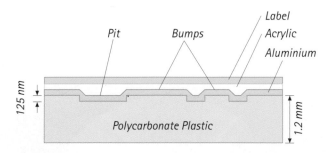

The pits and bumps on a CD surface.

Refraction also plays a part in how CDs work. There is a converging (convex) lens which focuses the laser beam into a tiny spot on the disc so that it can hit every single bump one at a time.

The code in the lines

Bar codes on the things we buy also work by reflection. The machine at the checkout has a laser which scans back and forth across the bar code, reflecting off the white patches but not off the black lines. This is another binary code and it identifies what the item is so that its cost can be added to your bill. The supermarket also counts everything that is sold so that the right replacement stock can be ordered. And if you use a loyalty card, the supermarket can make a note of everything you buy – and then send you special offer vouchers for products which fit in with your lifestyle!

QUESTIONS

1. What is a 'bio-reflector' made from?
2. Explain how the maximum amount of light is reflected from a bio-reflector.
3. How does a compact disc system use reflection?
4. What do we mean by 'binary code'?
5. How does a compact disc system use refraction?
6. What is the link between compact discs and supermarket bar codes?
7. List as many situations where we use reflection of visible light as you can think of. Make a second list of examples where other types of reflection are important.
8. Music CDs are made by pressing the pattern of bumps into the surface from a master disc. Research how a computer reads and writes information onto a CD.